Structured Qu
GCSE Biology

C. L. LIFFEN
MSc, MA, CBiol
Director of Studies,
Alleyn's School, London

C. F. LIFFEN
BSc, ARCS

HODDER AND STOUGHTON
LONDON SYDNEY AUCKLAND TORONTO

CONTENTS

PREFACE

The last twenty years have witnessed significant changes in the teaching of biology. Many of these have now been formally incorporated into the syllabuses for GCSE. Apart from the greater emphasis on practical and investigative work by the student, there has been a shift away from factual recall and rote learning. In its place is the handling of information (written, graphical and numerical) and a problem-solving approach. In devising these questions, we have tried to follow these principles and also to bring out the relevance of biology to the individual and society. We hope that we have also reflected the increased mathematical demands of the new examination.

The general aim of the book is to provide both teachers and pupils with further sources of questions that could be used for class tests, homework, revision work or to stimulate discussions.

The questions generally start with the presentation of material – in the form of a graph, table, data or a short passage. Then follows a series of short questions structured around the material. This form of questioning is extensively used at 16+ (and 18+) though the theme of the question is rarely pursued for more than 6–10 marks. The questions here have a minimum of 10 marks, more often 15–20, but hopefully relate more to the class situation where one is looking for material to consolidate upon a topic recently covered.

The exercises are organised into four sections in line with those of the National Criteria; the number in each section broadly reflects the amount of teaching time that would be allocated to that section. The general area for each question is indicated by the title though inevitably there may be some degree of overlap. Each exercise has a provisional mark scheme so that the pupils can allocate their time and energies appropriately.

No numerical answers are included where the pupils are asked to draw a graph from data as there will inevitably be some variation. The solidus has been used throughout rather than negative indices since this is more readily understood by most pupils.

Our thanks to John Clarke for his advice and encouragement, our desk editor Martin Finn, Jan Page for the cover design and all those pupils who acted as 'guinea pigs'.

C. L. Liffen
C. F. Liffen

1 Characteristics of vertebrates

1   Use the pictures below and your general knowledge of
    animals to copy and complete the table.   (12)

penguin

squirrel

frog

bat

shark

whale

	Penguin	Squirrel	Frog	Whale	Shark	Bat
Fur/hair on body?						
Fins present?						
Beak?						
Moist skin?						
Lay eggs in water?						
'Warm-blooded'?						

2   Give one characteristic that all of the animals in the pictures
    have in common?   (1)
3   Give two reasons why it is an advantage to be warm
    blooded?   (2)

Total 15 marks

1

2 Characteristics of invertebrates

The animals below were all collected from the same habitat.

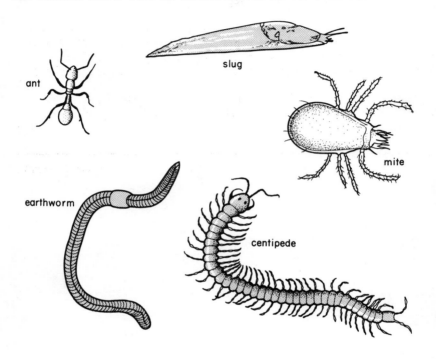

1 From what type of habitat were the organisms collected?   (2)
2 Copy and complete the table below to compare the five
   animals.   (12)

	Ant	Slug	Mite	Earth-worm	Centipede
Number of pairs of jointed legs present			4		
Does the animal have a segmented body?					Yes
Does the animal have antennae?		Yes			

2

3 Use the following key to place each animal in its correct group.

1   Body segments not visible and no legs ....*Molluscs*
       Segmented body visible...............................2
2   Jointed legs present....................................3
       No jointed legs...*Annelids*
3   More than 4 pairs of legs............................4
       4 pairs of legs or less 5
4   Body in two main parts, legs not all alike........*Crustaceans*
       Body of similar segments, legs alike................*Myriapods*
5   3 pairs of legs present ....*Insects*
       4 pairs of legs present ....*Arachnids*

(5)

4 Insects, arachnids and crustaceans all belong to the arthropod group. Give one characteristic that they have in common. *(1)*

Total 20 marks

3 Cell structure

The diagrams below show three different cells. Copy the table that follows. Use the diagrams and your general knowledge to complete the table.

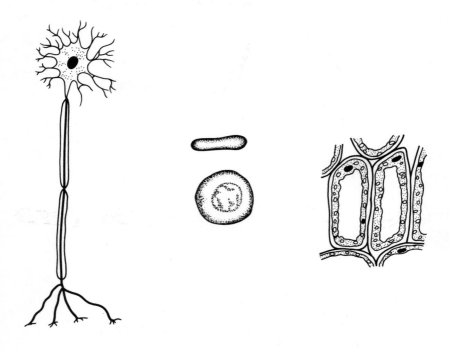

	Nerve cell	Red blood cell	Palisade cell
Cell wall present?	No		
Nucleus present?			Yes
Chloroplasts absent?	Yes		
Fatty sheath present?		No	
Vacuole absent?		Yes	

Total 10 marks

4

4 Bacteria

1(a) Name one characteristic of bacteria. *(1)*
  (b) Bacteria are important in the carbon and nitrogen cycles.
     Briefly explain why. *(2)*
2 Use the key to identify seven of the eight bacteria in the
   diagram. *(7)*

A   B   C   D

E   F   G   H

1	Cells spherical.........................2	
	Cells not spherical 3	
2	Cells in pairs...........................*Diplococcus*	
	Cells not in pairs.....................4	
3	Cells rod shaped.......................5	
	Cells not rod shaped.................6	
4	Cells form a chain.....................*Streptococcus*	
	Cells clumped together ....*Staphlyococcus aureus*	
5	Cells have hair-like projections.....*Salmonella typhi*	
	Cells without hair-like	
	projections ....*Mycobacterium tuberculosis*	
6	Cells comma shaped..................*Vibrio cholerae*	
	Cells spiral.............................*Treponema*	

Total 10 marks

5 A woodland food web

All plants are dependent on light from the sun. The photosynthetic material they produce is the basis of all food chains and food webs.

1(a) Plants need certain substances from their environment to carry out photosynthesis. Suggest what two of these substances might be. (2)

(b) Name two climatic factors which would influence the rate of photosynthesis. (2)

An oak tree has many different animals in it. The statements below describe some of their feeding relationships.

Spiders eat flies. Woodpeckers eat moth caterpillars and beetles. Nuthatches eat acorns. Aphids feed on juices from oak flowers. Beetles eat oak leaves. Sparrows eat aphids and moth caterpillars. Flies eat oak leaves and acorns. Squirrels eat oak leaves and acorns. Caterpillars eat oak flowers and leaves. Owls eat woodpeckers and blue tits. Hawks eat sparrows, woodpeckers and blue tits. Blue tits eat aphids, moth caterpillars, flies and spiders.

2   Starting with the oak tree, use the information above to construct a food web showing the feeding relationships of this community. (5)

3   Name one organism in your web that can be described as a
    (i) herbivore
    (ii) carnivore. (2)

4   What is the source of all the energy for this food web? (1)

5   Using your food web, write out a food chain with four organisms in it, starting with the producer. (1)

6   Draw a rough pyramid of numbers for your food chain. (2)

7(a) If all the hawks died, suggest two possible effects on the food web. Explain your answer fully. (4)

(b) If the flowers of the tree were not pollinated and fertilised, name two organisms whose numbers would be reduced. (2)

8   In winter the oak tree sheds its leaves and their nutrients are recycled. Explain carefully how their breakdown releases carbon dioxide back into the air. (4)

Total 25 marks

6 The carbon cycle

A balanced aquarium contains a variety of micro-organisms, plants and animals. There is no need to add food or any materials other than water. This is needed to replace the water lost by evaporation.

1   What is the source of energy in such an aquarium for the
    (i) plants
    (ii) animals
    (iii) micro-organisms?   (3)

The graph below shows how the amount of carbon dioxide dissolved in the water varied during a 24 hour period.

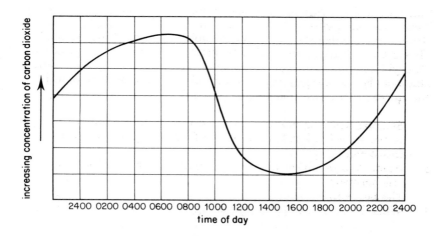

2(a) At what time of day was the carbon dioxide level
    (i) highest
    (ii) lowest?   (2)
  (b) Explain why the carbon dioxide level fell between 0800 and
    1400 hours.   (2)
3(a) Explain what would happen to the level of carbon dioxide if
    some more, larger animals were added to the aquarium.   (2)
  (b) What is the role of the micro-organisms in the aquarium?   (1)
4   Draw a diagram to show the circulation of the element
    carbon in a balanced aquarium.   (5)

Total 15 marks

7

7 Plant productivity

In this country a square metre of grassland receives about 1 million kilojoules of light energy per year. But the plants use very little of this directly in photosynthesis. About 50% is used in the evaporation of water, 32% passes through or between the leaves and is absorbed by the soil, another 15.8% is reflected from the leaves.

1   What percentage of the light is actually used by the plants in photosynthesis?   *(1)*
2   What is the effect of the light on the soil?   *(1)*
3   Explain how the loss of water from a leaf helps to reduce its temperature.   *(2)*

The light energy captured by plants is converted into chemical form. The total amount of energy fixed in photosynthesis is sometimes referred to as the *gross production* of the plant. Biologists often use another term, the *net production*. This is the amount of energy fixed in photosynthesis less the amount the plant uses up in respiration. This is the energy available to the plant to use in growth and to produce new materials for growth.

The figures below give some further information about what happens to the energy used in photosynthesis in one square metre of grassland per year.

Energy used (fixed) by the plants in photosynthesis	23 404 kJ
Energy used by the plants in respiration	1 968 kJ
Energy in dead leaves etc used by bacteria and fungi	14 863 kJ
Energy in leaves/roots eaten by rabbits and other small consumers	3 517 kJ

4(a) What is the gross production (in kJ) of the plants per year? *(1)*
 (b) What is the net production (in kJ) of the plants per year? *(2)*
5(a) Much of the net production of the plants passes to decomposers and small herbivores. If the remainder was eaten by a cow, how much energy would it get? *(2)*
 (b) What percentage of the net production is passed to the cow? *(2)*

The cow uses 1022 kJ of the energy from the plants for respiration and another 1909 kJ are lost in the faeces and urine of the animal.

6(a) How much is available for use in growth by the cow? (2)

(b) If 1 g of protein represents 17 kJ of energy, what mass (in grams) of protein would this amount of energy represent? (2)

(c) If the cow is grazing in a field of 12 000 m² with 3 other cows, by how much might its mass increase in one year? (3)

7 What assumption(s) did you make in order to answer the last question? (2)

Total 20 marks

8 Soil types

The quality of the soil is important for the growth of plants. It is especially important for crops, so that they grow well and give a high yield. The following procedure can be used to analyse soil.

An evaporating basin was weighed and then reweighed after a sample of soil was added. The basin was placed in an oven for twenty four hours and kept at a constant temperature of 95° C. After cooling it was weighed again to find the loss in mass. The results were as follows.

Mass of evaporating basin	51.5 g
Mass of evaporating basin + soil before drying	129.5 g
Mass of evaporating basin + soil after drying	110.5 g

1(a) Calculate the percentage water content of the soil. Show clearly all the steps in the calculation. *(4)*

 (b) Name two possible sources of error in the experimental method. *(2)*

Some of the dried soil was then placed in a crucible and heated strongly in a bunsen flame. After 40 minutes it was found that it had lost mass.

2(a) What material in the soil was being burnt off by the strong heating? *(1)*

 (b) What is this material formed from? *(1)*

 (c) How does this material affect the fertility and texture of the soil? *(2)*

The following experiment was set up to show that the fresh soil contained micro-organisms. The milk was boiled before it was added to the flask. The milk was allowed to cool before the soil was added.

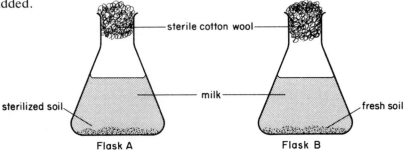

sterile cotton wool

milk

sterilized soil

fresh soil

Flask A   Flask B

3(a) Why was milk used and not water? *(1)*
  (b) After two days what difference would you expect to find in the contents of the two flasks? *(2)*
  (c) How would you account for these differences? *(2)*

Four samples of dried soil were analysed and the percentage mass of sand, clay and silt were recorded. The results are shown below.

		% by mass		
		Sand	Clay	Silt
Sample	A	60	20	20
Sample	B	10	70	20
Sample	C	50	30	20
Sample	D	40	20	40

4(a) Which soil would be slow to warm up? Explain your answer. *(2)*
  (b) Soil A has a large percentage of sand. How will this affect the soil's ability to retail water? *(1)*
  (c) What could be done to make the soil retain more water? *(1)*
  (d) Soil B contains a lot of clay which means it is heavy to work. What could be done to improve its properties? *(1)*

Total 20 marks

9 Leaf breakdown in soil

Leaves are broken down in the soil by a number of different organisms. The experiment below is one way of showing how fast they are broken down.

(a) Discs (1 cm in diameter) are cut from leaves using a cork borer.

(b) 20 discs are placed in a nylon mesh bag. Bags with various different mesh sizes are used. For example, the bag used to package fruit in supermarkets often has a mesh size of about 1 cm.

(c) The bags are then buried in fertile soil at a depth of about 5–10 cm.

(d) At six week intervals, they are dug up and examined to see how much material has disappeared.

Bags of two different mesh sizes were used in this investigation. In experiment A, a 7 mm mesh was used. In B, the mesh was 0.5 mm. Both bags were buried on the 1st July.

Time from burial (in days)	Percentage loss of leaf area in bag	
	Expt A	Expt B
0	0	0
42	20	8
84	70	17
126	86	28
168	90	30
210	93	33

1   Plot a graph of the data.   (5)
2   Which set of discs broke down at the fastest rate?   (1)
3   What is the percentage loss in leaf area after 100 days in
     (i) experiment A
     (ii) experiment B?   (2)
4   Bearing in mind the various types of animals to be found in fertile soil, which of these would be unable to enter the bag in experiment B?   (2)
5   What type of organisms do you think could be responsible for the disappearance of some of the leaf material from bag B?   (1)

6 How would you expect the result to differ if the bags
   (i) had been left on the soil surface
   (ii) had been buried at a depth of 1 metre instead of being
     buried at a depth of 5–10 cm?   (2)

7 Suggest two environmental factors which would affect the
rate of loss of leaf area in bag B.   (2)

8 How would you collect samples of animals found in the soil? (3)

9 How would the number and types of animals you obtained
in July differ from those collected in December?   (2)

Total 20 marks

10 Air pollution

The amount of carbon dioxide in the atmosphere has been recorded over a number of years. Mauna Loa in Hawaii is one place where very precise measurements are made. The data below give measurements of the level in the atmosphere since 1950. It is also possible to estimate how much carbon dioxide should be there as a result of burning fossil fuels such as coal. These estimates are also in the table below.

Year	1958	1962	1966	1970	1974	1978
Measured carbon dioxide (ppm)	315	317	319	325	329	334
Predicted carbon dioxide (ppm)	315	319	324	332	340	349

1 Draw a graph using the data above. *(6)*
2 Using your graph, how are the predicted level and the measured level of carbon dioxide between 1958 and 1978
   (i) similar
   (ii) different? *(2)*

Carbon dioxide often limits the rate of photosynthesis in natural habitats. It is also very soluble in water.

3 Give one possible explanation for the difference between the two sets of figures. *(1)*
4 Name one *biological* process that releases carbon dioxide into the atmosphere in very large quantities. *(1)*

A number of conservation groups claim that the level of carbon dioxide in the air will be twice its pre-industrial level by the year 2020 and that this will make the Earth suffer from the 'Greenhouse Effect'.

5(a) What is the 'Greenhouse Effect'? *(1)*
  (b) Give one possible result of the 'Greenhouse Effect' on the Earth. *(1)*

Carbon dioxide is not the only gas released when fuel is burnt. Various conservation groups claim that when such gases are dissolved in water in the atmosphere, acids may be formed. The

governments of Sweden and Norway claim that their rain is
becoming more acid due to the emissions from British power
stations. This is damaging forests and lakes. Lakes that have a high
acid level are clear, with very little plant or animal life in them.
Lakes that are not acidic are quite cloudy. Recently, the Central
Electricity Generating Board (CEGB) began experimenting with a
treatment for lakes in this country which have high acid levels. The
CEGB is spraying the vegetation and soil surrounding the lake with
lime. When it rains the lime will slowly dissolve and run into the
water.

6   Which gas (other than carbon dioxide) that is released by
    power stations contributes to the formation of the acid rain? *(1)*
7   State one effect of the acid rain in Scandinavia.   *(1)*
8   Suggest one way in which the gas may affect humans.   *(1)*
9(a) How will spraying the surrounding vegetation and soil with
    lime help to reduce the acidity of the lake?   *(2)*
  (b) How will reducing the acidity effect the oxygen level of the
    lake?   *(1)*

Lead is also a major atmospheric pollutant. Scientists in Greenland
have shown that ice formed in 1750 had only a quarter of the lead
in ice formed in 1940. Between 1940 and 1968 the lead level in the
ice increased by 300%.

10 Why have the lead levels risen so rapidly between 1940 and
    1968?   *(1)*
11 Suggest one way in which the atmospheric lead levels may
    be reduced.   *(1)*

Total 20 marks

11 Water pollution

1   Water is essential for life. Give two ways in which water is
     used in living organisms.   (2)

Unfortunately we are polluting our water supplies. Two of the most
common pollutants are nitrates and phosphates. This is partly due to
the increase in the use of chemical fertilizers since the 1950's. It is
estimated that in Britain only half the nitrogen applied to the land
in the form of fertilizers is taken up by the crops. Much is washed
away by rain and drains through the soil. The level of nitrogen in
rivers such as the Great Ouse doubled between 1958 and 1968. The
figures below show the oxygen and nitrate levels in the Rhine,
which is probably the most polluted river in Europe.

	1959	1964	1971
Oxygen (mg/l)	5.9	5.4	4.5
Nitrate (mg/l)	8.4	10.7	12.0

2(a) Draw a histogram of the data.   (5)
 (b) Calculate the
     (i) percentage decrease in oxygen level
     (ii) percentage increase in nitrate level between 1959 and
          1971.   (2)
 (c) What happens to the level of oxygen as the nitrate level
     increases?   (1)

The nitrates and phosphates encourage the growth of unicellular
plants (algae) in the surface layers of the water. Very large numbers
of algae prevent light reaching the lower levels of the water. When
they die, their remains are broken down by micro-organisms. This
process uses up large quantities of the dissolved oxygen in the
water. Fish and other organisms that have a high oxygen
requirement die and are also broken down by micro-organisms
which increases the problem. Lough Neagh in Northern Ireland is a
fresh water lake. Water returned to the lake has a high level of
phosphates due to the use of detergent washing powders. This has
resulted in the growth of large numbers of photosynthetic blue-green
algae, which have blocked the water treatment machinery that
provides Belfast with water and have threatened the freshwater life
of the lake.

3 In unpolluted waters the algae do not grow so quickly. What do you think limits their growth? *(1)*

4 What group of organisms will be mainly responsible for the decay and decomposition of the algae and later the fish? *(1)*

5 How would the presence of large numbers of algae in the surface waters affect the photosynthetic activity of larger and deeper rooted plants growing in a lake? *(2)*

6 Explain how the death of the algae would affect other organisms in a fresh water lake. *(3)*

In the Philippines, using fertilizers on the paddy fields has affected the local lakes and so the nearby villages have lost a readily available source of fish.

7(a) If algae in the lake used up most of the oxygen, how might this affect the fish? *(1)*

(b) What important item in the diet would fish supply in a third world country like the Philippines? *(1)*

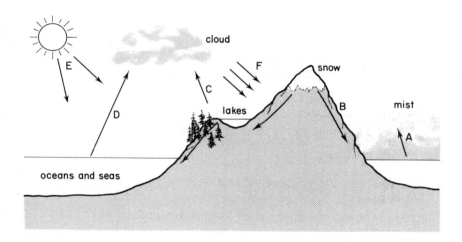

8 Match the statements below to the letters on the diagram of the water cycle above. You can use each letter once, more than once or not at all.
  (i) Evaporation of water.
  (ii) Transpiration of water by the organism.
  (iii) The energy source for water evaporation.
  (iv) Precipitation of water. *(4)*

9 Name two ways in which industry or agriculture makes use of water. *(2)*

Total 25 marks

12 Sewage and water pollution

When raw sewage is poured into a river, the water soon loses much of its oxygen. The oxygen is used up by bacteria, which break down the sewage. The sewage produced by a single human being in one day needs 115 g of oxygen to break it down. A litre of water at 5 °C holds about 13 mg of oxygen. As the temperature of water goes up, the amount of oxygen falls. Various ways of dealing with sewage have been used. Nowadays, most sewage is treated before it is emptied into rivers. This involves oxidation by aerobic organisms – the activated sludge process. This produces a clear effluent and sewage sludge. The latter can be dried and then used as fertilizer. The clean effluent can sometimes cause other problems as it is often rich in nitrate and phophate. At holiday resorts such as Blackpool and Great Yarmouth, raw (untreated) sewage is discharged into the sea. The point of discharge may be some way out to sea, but tide action and wind can bring the sewage back to the shoreline. Raw sewage is a health hazard. At one resort, levels of 10 000 bacterial cells per cm^3 of sea water have been found. Guidelines set by the European Economic Community (EEC) recommend levels no higher than 2000 bacterial cells per cm^3 sea water.

1 How many litres of water would be needed to provide the oxygen to break down the faeces produced by one person per day? Show clearly how you work out your answer. (3)
2 Give two differences between raw (untreated) sewage and treated sewage? (2)
3(a) Why is sewage in the sea especially hazardous at places like Great Yarmouth, Blackpool and Southend? (2)
 (b) The amount of sewage being discharged into the sea increases during the summer. Why do you think this is? (1)
4 How many times greater is the bacterial cell level at the resort tested than the EEC guidelines? (1)
5(a) What is the main nitrogen-containing compound found in urine? (1)
 (b) What would be the long term effects of releasing sewage into a river or lake? (2)
6 Given a supply of nutrient agar plates (and any usual laboratory equipment), how could you demonstrate that bacteria were present in sea water? (3)

Total 15 marks

13 The polio virus

In most people, infection by the polio virus results in an intestinal disturbance which has few or no symptoms. However, in some people the virus causes paralysis when the virus moves from the intestine into the nervous system.

1   Why are viruses considered to be parasites?   (1)

2(a) How could the virus travel from the intestine to the nervous
     system?   (1)

 (b) Which blood cells are responsible for the formation of
     antibodies against the virus?   (1)

 (c) Where are these cells produced?   (1)

The disease is world wide. It is transmitted by dust and faecal contact, especially in areas of poor hygiene and sanitation. It is now rare in this country because of vaccination against polio which started in the early 1950's using the Salk vaccine. This involves injection of the 'dead' virus. Priority was given to children and young adults because adults over forty are far less likely to develop the disease. There were certain disadvantages in using the Salk vaccine. Firstly the immunity that it provided declined with time and secondly it had to be given by injection. Large scale inoculation can be a problem in developing countries. The vaccine worked by stimulating the production of antibodies in the blood. It was successful in preventing infection of the nervous system and the risk of paralysis. It did not prevent the intestinal infection and so could not control epidemics.

3   Why do you think that adults over forty were less likely to
    develop polio?   (2)

4   What particular difficulties do you think developing
    countries had in using the Salk vaccine?   (2)

Later the Sabin vaccine was introduced. This vaccine consists of weakened living viruses. It is taken by mouth and is extremely effective in controlling the intestinal infection. In this country nearly all children are vaccinated in their first year of life.

5   Suggest two ways in which the Sabin vaccine was an
    improvement on the Salk vaccine.   (2)

Total 10 marks

19

14 Antibiotics

A patient suffering from very severe toothache had an abscess erupt through his gum. A sample of the pus from this was cultured on a nutrient agar in a Petri dish. A multodisc, which had samples of five different antibiotics was placed on the nutrient agar. The two halves of the Petri dish were then sellotaped together, it was turned upside down and placed in an incubator at 30 °C. The diagram below shows the Petri dish after incubation. Shading shows where the organisms have grown:

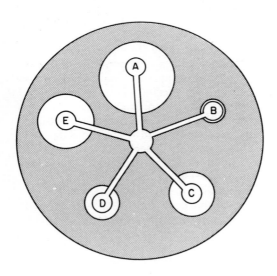

A = penicillin
B = polymixin
C = metronidazole
D = tetracycline
E = streptomycin

1   What is an antibiotic?   (2)
2(a) The patient was allergic to penicillin, so which antibiotic
     should the patient be given?   (1)
 (b) Explain your choice of antibiotic for this patient.   (1)
 (c) The organisms causing this infection appear to be resistant
     to one of these antibiotics. Which one?   (1)
3   Why was the Petri dish
       (i) sellotaped
      (ii) turned upside down
     (iii) incubated?   (3)
4(a) What nutrients would be present in the agar?   (1)
 (b) Why are these nutrients needed for the growth of bacteria?   (1)

The patient was given a five day course of the appropriate antibiotic. This had to be taken at regular 8 hour intervals during the day.

5(a) Why do they have to be taken at regular intervals? (1)
  (b) Why is it important to finish the course of antibiotics even if you feel better? (1)
  (c) Explain how bacteria may become resistant to certain antibiotics. Include the following words in your explanation: *mutation, selection, resistance.* (3)
6   In the early part of this century, spider's webs (on which many fungal spores were trapped) were placed on minor cuts and wounds. Suggest
     (i) one reason why this might have been a useful procedure
     (ii) one reason why it could have been dangerous. (2)
7   Describe in outline how you would culture one particular species of fungus from a mixture of different species of fungi present in a soil sample. (3)

Total 20 marks

15 AIDS

Acquired immune deficiency syndrome (AIDS) is caused by the Human Immuno-deficiency Virus, HIV. HIV invades and damages those blood cells that would normally destroy viruses and bacteria. Though the body produces antibodies in response to the virus, they are ineffective. These antibodies can be detected by a blood test. This is the only way in which one can tell if someone has been infected with the HIV. Infected individuals may show no signs of infection and feel quite well but they are capable of passing it on to others. They are described as carriers. By the end of 1986 over 40 000 people were thought to have been infected in Great Britain.

1(a) What type of blood cells are infected by the AIDS virus?   *(1)*
  (b) By what means can HIV carriers be identified?   *(1)*

In most viral infections the incubation period is short, that is, the time from infection to the appearance of disease symptoms. HIV has a long incubation period. Throughout this time, the virus is present in body fluids.There are three main ways in which the HIV can be passed from one person to another.
a. Through sexual intercourse (either anal or vaginal) when semen (carrying the virus) comes into contact with blood. This could occur if capillaries are broken or damaged when the penis is introduced.
b. By passing infected blood into a healthy person.
c. By an infected mother passing it to her baby before or during birth.
The virus is present in body fluids such as blood, semen, saliva or tears. However, no one has caught AIDS from saliva or tears. All cases reported have been caused by blood or semen. Fortunately HIV is not a hardy virus and does not last very long outside the body. In the past, some people were given blood or blood products (for example blood clotting factors) which had been infected with the HIV. Haemophiliacs, in particular, caught the virus in this way. Now in this country, all donated blood is tested before it is used and blood products are heat treated to reduce the risk of infection.

2   How can the following help reduce the risk of infection with HIV
     (i) using a condom (sheath) during sexual intercourse
     (ii) reducing the number of sexual partners?   *(4)*
3(a) Intra-venous drug abusers often share needles or syringes.
    Explain why this practice can help spread the virus.   *(2)*

(b) Why should women who are intra-venous drug abusers avoid
   becoming pregnant? *(1)*

4 Some HIV carriers were banned from using a local
   swimming pool. Explain if there was any risk of other
   swimmers catching the virus? *(2)*

Eventually, the HIV damages the body's immune system so much
that the infected person cannot fight any invading micro-organisms.
Death is often due to a form of pneumonia or cancer. The table
below shows the number of AIDS cases in different risk groups in
Great Britain up to the end of 1986. People who are carriers but
without symptoms are not included.

Risk group	Number of cases		Total cases	Number of deaths
	Male	Female		
Homosexuals/bisexuals	538	0	538	244
Intra-venous drug abusers	7	2	9	2
Intra-venous drug abuser and homosexual	6	0	6	4
Haemophiliacs	25	0	25	19
Recipient of blood transfusion	6	4	10	9
Heterosexuals	10	8	18	12
Child born to AIDS-infected mother	0	2	3	2
Other	1	1	1	1

5(a) How many
   (i) males
   (ii) females
   were reported as having AIDS by the end of 1986? *(2)*
  (b) How many people had died as a result of AIDS by the end
   of 1986? *(1)*

6 At present homosexual/bisexual men are more likely to
   become infected with the AIDS virus. Explain why this is. *(2)*

7(a) Why have a number of haemophiliacs developed AIDS? *(1)*
  (b) Are haemophiliacs still at risk from this source of infection? *(1)*

If the number of recorded cases of a disease keeps rising
dramatically it is described an an *epidemic*.

8 What evidence is there that the number of AIDS cases will
   reach epidemic proportions? *(2)*

Total 20 marks

16 Diseases in prisons

Many prisons were built during the last century and are now rather old. They often have poor ventilation and are rather damp. The inmates, like the rest of us, suffer from a variety of diseases and illnesses. Long stay prisoners in five different prisons were surveyed to see what illnesses were common. Some of the results of the survey are shown below:

| | Prison | | | | |
	1	2	3	4	5
	(number of cases per year)				
Bronchitis	9	13	4	15	11
Heart disease	3	11	0	29	1
Food poisoning	0	31	11	8	27
Goitre	21	1	0	1	2
Tuberculosis	3	4	0	0	24
Typhoid	0	0	20	0	0

1   For each prison, find the total number of cases of all
    illnesses per year. Draw a bar chart of your results.   (5)
2   Which prison has the highest number of cases of
      (i) heart disease
      (ii) food poisoning
      (iii) goitre?   (3)
3   Which of the diseases in the list is usually linked with
      (i) an inadequate diet
      (ii) poor hygiene?   (2)
4   Why does
      (i) over-crowding
      (ii) poor ventilation   (4)
    contribute to the spread of disease?
5   Why were long stay prisoners used in the survey?   (1)

Total 15 marks

17 Holly parasites

A gall is an abnormal growth produced by a plant in response to an infection by a parasite. One parasite that produces galls is the holly leaf miner *Phytomyza ilicis*. The adult insect is a small fly which lays its eggs in June at the base of holly leaves. At first only a small swollen area shows that the leaf has been infected. A larva hatches from the egg and begins to eat the internal tissue along the midrib of the leaf. The plant responds by forming some new tissue within the leaf, causing the surface of the leaf to bulge. Such leaves may be further damaged by birds trying to open the leaves to feed on the insects. The larva then moves into the mesophyll tissue of the leaf. As a result a discoloured patch forms on the leaf. The larva pupates in the following March and the adult fly emerges from the leaf in May or June to repeat the cycle. New holly leaves continue to be formed throughout the summer months.

1 Explain what is meant by the term parasite.   (2)
2 Use the information in the passage to complete the
   following: Draw a circle and divide it into twelve equal
   segments to represent the months of the year. Label these
   clearly and then mark on when the different stages of the
   insect's life cycle are found on or in the leaves.   (4)
3 The mesophyll cells contain many chloroplasts. What effect
   might the leaf miner's activities have on the growth of the
   plant?   (2)

The leaf miner may be parasitised itself by a species of very small wasp. The adult wasp lays its eggs, singly, inside the body of a leaf miner larva. When the wasp eggs hatch, their larvae eat the tissues of the leaf miner which then dies.

4 Draw a rough pyramid of numbers of the holly leaves, leaf
   miners and wasps.   (2)
5 Which organism could be described as a primary consumer?   (1)
6 Suggest one factor which would prevent all the leaves on a
   holly bush from becoming infected by leaf miners.   (2)
7 If all the leaf miner larvae were to be parasitised by wasps,
   what would happen to the wasp population in the following
   year?   (2)

Total 15 marks

18 Biological control

In the late 1800's, the cottony-cushion scale insect was accidentally introduced to California from Australia. Its numbers increased so much that the orange-growing industry was threatened. The insecticides then available did not kill the scale insects. Growers decided to use a form of biological control. They introduced a type of ladybird which was a natural predator of the scale insect in Australia. It ate the scale insects and the orange-growing industry was saved.

1   Apart from being a predator of the scale insects, what was another important characteristic that the ladybird had to possess? *(1)*

2   Why did the number of scale insects increase so dramatically in California before the introduction of the ladybird? *(2)*

By 1945, new types of insecticide had been developed. One of these, DDT, was used to spray the orange groves. But it was found that the ladybirds were more likely to die from the effects of the DDT than the scale insects.

3   What do you think was the effect of this? *(2)*

4   Why is it better to use biological control rather than chemical insecticides? *(1)*

The rabbit has been a pest of arable crops and grassland in Europe for hundreds of years. Its nuisance value was offset to some extent as it provided a source of food and fur. Attempts were made (in the early 1950's) to control the rabbit population by the introduction of a viral disease — myxomatosis. This disease was found in populations of rabbits in South America. It is passed on by the rabbit flea. Rabbits normally live underground in crowded warrens. A small percentage of the population live above ground in nests. The rabbit population decreased rapidly within a few years. Areas of grassland which had previously been grazed by the rabbits began to change, tree seedlings appeared and established themselves. Carnivores such as foxes, stoats and weasels found that a major item in their diet had largely disappeared.

5   Which of the organisms mentioned in the passage above are
    (i) parasites
    (ii) secondary consumers? *(5)*

6 Which would you expect to find in greater numbers, rabbits or fleas? Explain your answer. *(2)*

7 What do you think happened to the numbers of carnivores when the rabbit population fell? *(1)*

8 Why do you think myxomatosis was introduced? *(1)*

9(a) The numbers of rabbits are now increasing again although myxomatosis is still present. Why do you think that so many of the rabbits died when the disease was first introduced? *(2)*

(b) What explanation can you give for the current increase in numbers of rabbits? *(2)*

Aphids cause damage to many types of crop plant. They insert their piercing mouthparts into the food channels (phloem) of the plants to draw off some of the sugars they are carrying. Aphids do not usually kill the host plant by such activities but they may introduce viruses and bacteria into the plants and so spread disease. In greenhouses, the numbers of aphids may be controlled by introducing ladybirds. Ladybirds prefer to eat aphids rather than anything else.

10 Parasites do not usually kill their hosts. Why? *(1)*

11 Give two possible effects of the feeding activities of the aphids on a host plant. *(2)*

12 Why are ladybirds more efficient at controlling aphid populations in a confined space, like a greenhouse? *(2)*

Money spiders are also important in controlling the number of aphids in wheat fields. They move into the wheat fields in early spring from surrounding hedgerows. They weave large, non-sticky webs between the stalks of the wheat plants. Many more webs are made at the time of flowering and grain production. This is the time when the aphid populations also increase. The spiders' webs collect many of the aphids which fall off the plants or are knocked off by other predators. By early July, up to 16% of the aphid population may fall into the webs each day. Not all of these are eaten although the hungry spiders tend to eat the larger aphids. Only when the aphid population is large do the ladybirds move into the wheat fields to feed.

13 Why do the spiders live in the hedgerows during the early part of the year? *(2)*

14 Why does the
    (i) aphid population
    (ii) spider population
    increase at the time of flowering and grain production? *(4)*

Total 30 marks

19 Yeast and single cell protein

The figures below show the increase in the number of yeast cells growing in a liquid culture medium over 20 hours. The culture was maintained at a constant temperature.

Time (hours)	Number of yeast cells (millions per cm³)
2	20
4	40
6	85
8	200
10	375
12	535
14	620
16	660
18	670
20	670

1   Plot a graph using the data above. (5)
2   What was the number of yeast cells per cm^3 after
    (i) 8 hours
    (ii) 15 hours? (2)
3(a) How many hours does it take for the number of yeast cells to become constant? (1)
  (b) Suggest two reasons why the number of cells does not increase any more after 18 hours. (2)
4   Name two substances that the yeast absorbs from the culture solution. (2)
5   Which product of yeast's respiratory activities is important in
    (i) brewing
    (ii) bread making? (2)

Other species of yeast can be used to make animal foodstuffs. Many industrial and farming processes produce waste material. These wastes can cause pollution if discharged into rivers. It is possible to make use of the waste to grow yeast cells. For example, potato processing factories produce a lot of water containing starch. This starch-rich water is sterilised. It is then passed into large fermenters.

These contain a type of yeast which can break down the starch to simpler carbohydrates.

6   Why is water from the potato processing factory likely to contain starch?   *(1)*

7   How could you test a sample of water to show that starch is present?   *(2)*

8   What might be the effects of adding large quantities of warm starch-rich water to a river?   *(3)*

9   Why is the starch rich water sterilised?   *(1)*

When the breakdown of starch is complete, the sugar rich solution is then passed to another fermenter with a different species of yeast. This yeast grows rapidly using up the simple carbohydrates. The yeast cells are then harvested, dried and stored in bulk. These dried cells are rich in protein and vitamins and can be used as animal food supplements. Tests have shown that they are quite safe for use with pigs, chickens and calves as a high protein food source.

10   The dried yeast cells have been shown to be acceptable as an animal food material but humans are unwilling to eat them. Suggest one reason for this?   *(1)*

11   Why is protein so important in the diet of animals and humans?   *(2)*

12   What other types of micro-organisms can be grown in culture like yeast cells?   *(1)*

Total 25 marks

20 Protease activity

An experiment was set up to look at the action of protease (an enzyme) on gelatine (a protein). Pieces of gelatine containing a red dye were placed in test tubes as shown below. Each test tube contained the same mass of gelatine.

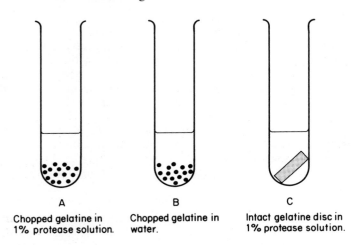

A
Chopped gelatine in 1% protease solution.

B
Chopped gelatine in water.

C
Intact gelatine disc in 1% protease solution.

All the test tubes were placed in a water bath at 25 °C.

1(a) Was the surface area of the gelatine greatest in test tube A or test tube C? *(1)*
 (b) In which tube would most dye be released? Explain your answer. *(3)*
2   Why was tube B included in the experiment? *(2)*
3(a) Use the results of the experiment to explain why you should chew your food well. *(2)*
 (b) Name one protease in the human alimentary canal that could digest gelatine. *(1)*
4(a) What would the result for tube A have been if the enzyme had been boiled before it was added to the test tube? Explain why this would happen. *(2)*
 (b) Design a simple experiment to investigate how protease activity varies with temperature. *(4)*

Total 15 marks

21 Biological washing powders

Many washing powders are described as biological because they contain an enzyme which acts on protein based stains. This enzyme is a protease extracted from bacteria such as *Bacillus subtilis*. For the washing powder to work best, it needs mild alkaline conditions, a suitable temperature (between 45 °C and 55 °C) and the presence of a detergent.

1   Give two examples of stains which a biological washing powder would not remove from clothing?   (2)
2   If the temperature of the wash was raised to 70 °C, do you think the protease would work quicker or slower? Explain your answer.   (2)
3   Would the protease work quicker or slower if the washing powder was slightly acidic? Explain your answer.   (2)
4   Some fabrics, such as silk and wool (made up of animal protein) should be hand washed in soap powders. If they are machine washed then the cycle should be short. Explain why.   (2)

To obtain the enzyme in large enough amounts, the bacteria are grown in large stainless steel vessels. These are sterilised and then a sterile 'broth' containing potato starch, ground up soya beans, mineral salts and water is added. The vessels are oxygenated continuously. A small number of bacteria are then added. When the bacteria have finished growing and have used the nutrients in the 'broth', they and any other solid material are filtered off, leaving an enzyme-rich solution. The enzyme is separated out from this and dried to a powder. Finally, a detergent is added.

5   Why are the vessels and the 'broth' sterilised before the bacteria are added?   (1)
6   Which of the nutrients provides a source of
     (i) carbohydrate
    (ii) amino acids
    for the bacteria?   (2)
7   Why do you think oxygen is provided?   (1)
8   Sketch a rough graph to show how the numbers of the bacteria would change while being grown in the vessels.   (3)

Total 15 marks

22 Starch breakdown

Human salivary amylase can break down starch. The speed at which it acts depends upon temperature. The data below are the results of an experiment to find out how much the activity of amylase varied with temperature. Six test tubes were set up each containing 5 cm^3 of starch. At the start of the experiment, 1 cm^3 of amylase was added to each tube. The breakdown of starch was followed by using a chemical test.

Temperature (°C)	20	25	30	35	40	45
Time taken for starch to disappear (s)	601	315	216	180	198	417

1   Plot a graph of these results. *(5)*
2   At what temperature does the amylase work best? *(1)*
3   At the start of the experiment why was the same amount of starch and amylase used in each of the six test tubes? *(1)*
4   Chemical reactions usually get faster as the temperature rises. Why does the breakdown of starch in this experiment slow down above 40 °C? *(1)*
5   What chemical test could you use to show that the starch has disappeared? *(2)*
6(a) Name one other factor that would affect the rate at which salivary amylase works. *(1)*
  (b) How would you test the hypothesis that the salivary amylase of smokers is less active than that of non-smokers? *(4)*

Total 15 marks

23 A model gut

An experiment was set up as follows:
Visking (dialysis) tubing was knotted at one end and then filled with a mixture of starch and glucose solution. The outside of the tubing was washed. Then the tubing and its contents were placed in distilled water in a boiling tube as shown in the diagram below. Immediately, a sample of the distilled water was taken and tested for starch and glucose. The tubing and its contents were left in the distilled water for 20 minutes. After this time, another sample of the water surrounding the tubing was tested for starch and glucose.

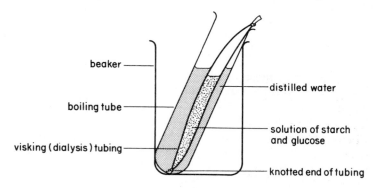

1(a) This apparatus is often described as a 'model gut'. What does
    (i) the Visking (dialysis) tubing represent?
    (ii) the distilled water represent? (2)
 (b) List two ways in which the human gut differs from the tubing used in the experiment? (2)
2 Why was the tubing washed after adding the starch and sugar solution? (1)
3 Carefully describe how you would test for starch. (2)
4 Why were the tubing and its contents left for 20 minutes? (1)
5(a) When the water was tested after 20 minutes, what results would you expect? (2)
 (b) How would you explain the result? (3)
6(a) At what temperature do you think the experiment should be carried out? (1)
 (b) Explain why you have chosen this temperature. (1)

Total 15 marks

24 Fluoride and teeth

The amount of fluoride present naturally in drinking water varies considerably. In some areas there is none, whereas others have more than 8 parts per million (ppm). A survey was done in different regions of the United States, all of which had different levels of fluoride in the drinking water. In each area, the teeth of all the 13 year olds were looked at and then the average number of decayed teeth per child calculated. The results were as follows:

Fluoride level in drinking water (ppm)	0.2	0.5	1.0	1.5	2.0	2.5
Average number of decayed teeth per child	8.0	4.8	2.8	2.2	1.95	1.90

1(a) Plot a graph of these results. (5)
  (b) What is the average number of decayed teeth (to the nearest whole number) you might expect to find in a child's mouth if the fluoride level was
    (i) 1.75 ppm
    (ii) 0.65 ppm? (2)

Adding fluoride to the drinking water supply is controversial. It can be expensive and some people say it is wasteful and/or dangerous. Very high levels of fluoride are poisonous and levels higher than 1.5 ppm can discolour the teeth. Nevertheless, some Local Authorities add fluoride, so that the level in the drinking water supply is brought up to 1 ppm.

2(a) Why do you think this level (1 ppm) was chosen? (2)
  (b) Why should the addition of fluoride to the water supply be thought wasteful? (2)
  (c) Give two arguments
    (i) in favour of adding fluoride to drinking water
    (ii) against adding fluoride to drinking water. (4)
3(a) Suggest two other factors which might affect the amount of dental decay in children. (2)
  (b) Briefly outline how you might investigate one of these factors. (3)
4   Use the following words to explain how dental decay is caused.
        sugar   plaque   enamel   bacteria   acid (5)

Total 25 marks

25 Pig nutrition and growth

At one time pigs used to be fed with swill, scraps and left-overs from human meals. Nowadays they are often fed on specially prepared pellets. These are made from cereals, bran and dried fish or meat. Vitamins and minerals are then added.

A new born pig weighs about 1.2 kg, by the time of slaughter its mass will have increased to 100 kg. For the first 6 weeks, they are fed on milk from their mother. After 6 weeks they are put onto solid food (pellets). This is termed *weaning*. By this time they weigh about 25 kg. From the time of weaning to the time that they are killed each will have eaten 300 kg of pellets.

1 How much on average did the pigs' mass increase per week during the first 6 weeks? (2)

2 What was the gain in mass between weaning and slaughter? (1)

3 Which of the ingredients in the pellets would provide
   (i) protein only
   (ii) both protein and carbohydrate? (2)

The composition of pig pellets is as follows:
   16% protein
   74% carbohydrate
   6% fibre
   3% fat
   1% vitamins and minerals

4 How much protein did the pig obtain from the pellets? (1)

5 If only about 13% of the pig's body is protein, what mass (in kilograms) of protein is there in the pig's body when it is killed? (1)

6 If only 70% of the carcass can be used by humans for food, how many kilograms of protein can we obtain from a pig, assuming the protein is evenly spread through the pig's body? (2)

7 How much of the protein that the pig ate does not get passed on to humans? (1)

Total 10 marks

26 Protein sources

The table below shows the amount of protein produced per hectare for different plant and animal sources.

Source	Protein yield (kg/hectare)
Soya bean	510
Rice	198
Wheat	150
Milk	50
Pigs	30
Beef	25

1(a) From the table, do plant or animal sources give the greatest yield of protein per hectare? *(1)*
 (b) Give one reason why the yield is greater from this source. *(1)*

The following table shows the amount of protein taken in each day from plant and animal sources in different continents.

Continent	Protein intake (g/person/day) Animal	Plant
Africa	11	38
Asia	10	37
Europe	49	37
North America	66	33

2 For each of the continents in the table, calculate the percentage of the total protein intake that comes from plant sources. *(4)*
3(a) Which continent has the lowest percentage intake of plant protein in the diet? Suggest a reason for this. *(2)*
 (b) Which continent has the highest percentage intake of plant protein in the diet? Suggest a reason. *(2)*

Although animals cannot make amino acids (the building blocks of protein), they can in some cases convert one amino acid into another. There are, however, some eight amino acids which cannot be made in this way and must be gained directly from the diet.

These are called essential amino acids. Plant proteins often lack one or more of these essential amino acids. For example, protein derived from cereals lacks the amino acid lysine. Soya beans contain little methionine. Animal protein from almost any source contains all the essential amino acids. It is generally accepted that an average adult male needs about 36 g of such protein a day, an average adult female about 30 g.

4(a) Using the table, in which continents is the minimum high quality protein requirement not met? *(2)*

(b) Why is the protein requirement of an average female less than that of an average male? *(1)*

5(a) What might happen to an individual whose diet lacked one or more of these essential amino acids? *(1)*

(b) Some vegetarians refuse to eat anything of animal origin, including milk or eggs. How can they ensure they gain enough of the different types of essential amino acids? *(1)*

Total 15 marks

27 Food additives

Over the past few years, people's eating habits in Britain have changed a lot. Not long ago sliced white bread was very popular. White bread is made from grain that has had all the outer layers removed. The bread includes large amounts of preservatives and additives, like bleaching agents and vitamins. Now more people are changing to wholegrain breads. It is now possible to buy white bread 'with added fibre' which some people prefer to wholegrain bread.

1(a) Why are preservatives added to bread bought in shops but not to home-made bread? (1)
 (b) What does a bleaching agent do? (1)
2 Name two substances that are present in greater amounts in wholegrain bread than in white bread. (2)
3(a) Why should we want bread to be high in fibre? (2)
 (b) Name one other food that is high in fibre. (1)

Nowadays the ingredients of different food products must be listed so that the shopper can see what is in them. The contents of two different makes of strawberry jam are shown below.

Jar A	Jar B
Strawberries	Strawberries
Sugar	Concentrated grape juice
Glucose syrup	Concentrated apple juice
Gelling agent (liquid pectin)	Gelling agent (pectin)
Acidity regulator E330	
Colours E110, E124	
Total sugar content 66 g per 100 g	Made with no added sugar

4(a) A shopper bought jar B thinking it did not contain any sugar at all. Explain how you could test the two jams to show whether this was true. (3)
 (b) Why are grape and apple juice added to jam B? (1)
5 Which jam do you think your dentist would recommend? Explain your answer. (2)

Some food additives are given E numbers, which are the same in all the countries of the European Economic Community (EEC). Not all substances with E numbers are artificial products, for example E300 is vitamin C.

6   Which two E number additives are only included to make the jam more attractive to the shopper?   *(2)*

Until recently the colouring E102 was frequently found in foods, especially those intended for children. Now many manufacturers have stopped using it.

7(a) What is the name of the chemical known as E102?   *(1)*
  (b) Give one reason why it was added to foods and drinks.   *(1)*
  (c) Why has E102 been removed?   *(1)*

Antibiotics are only usually used for treating diseases. But there are a few that are used to preserve food. One of these, *nisin*, is used for canning and in some cheese products. It has a very low toxicity.

8   Explain why problems may arise from using nisin as a food preservative.   *(2)*

Total 20 marks

28 The heart

The diagram below shows a human heart that has been cut across in the region of the ventricles.

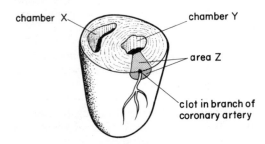

chamber X

chamber Y

area Z

clot in branch of coronary artery

1 Use the diagram to decide which of the structures (labelled X and Y) is the left ventricle? Give a reason for your choice. *(2)*

2(a) Which two chambers of the heart are not shown on the diagram? *(1)*

(b) Give one difference between the blood in ventricle X and that in ventricle Y. *(1)*

(c) When ventricle X contracts, where will the blood go? *(1)*

3 What type of tissue makes up the wall of the heart? *(1)*

The coronary arteries supply the wall of the heart with blood. A small branch of one of these is shown in the diagram. If a clot forms at the point shown then the area around it (which is shaded), will die as blood can no longer reach this region.

4 Name three substances which the blood will normally supply to cells in this area. *(3)*

A man aged 47 says he is worried about the risk of heart disease. He works in an office and gets very little exercise. He is 25 kg overweight, smokes and eats lots of fried food.

5 He makes the following suggestions. Would you agree or disagree with him. Explain your answers.
   (i) He will start playing a very strenuous sport like squash.
   (ii) He will not eat fried food.
   (iii) He will smoke more because it stops him feeling hungry. *(6)*

Total 15 marks

29 Blood cells

The table shows the composition of the blood of three different volunteers.

	Red blood cells per mm^3	White blood cells per mm^3	Thrombocytes/ platelets per mm^3
Person A	7 500 000	560	250 000
Person B	5 100 000	6 100	260 000
Person C	2 200 000	5 000	500

1(a) One of the people has too little iron in their diet. Which person do you think it is? Explain your choice. *(2)*
 (b) Iron deficiency causes anaemia. Give one symptom of it. *(1)*
 (c) Suggest one food that is rich in iron. *(1)*
 (d) Why do pregnant women need extra iron? *(1)*
2(a) One of the people in the table has blood which will take a long time to clot. Who do you think it is? *(1)*
 (b) Explain your choice. *(1)*
3(a) When the body is fighting an infection there is an increase in the number of one type of blood cell. Which type of cell will increase? *(1)*
 (b) Where are these cells made in the body? *(1)*

To get the samples of blood, a doctor first wiped the skin of each volunteer's thumb with cotton wool soaked in alcohol (ethanol). Then the doctor pricked the thumb with a sterile needle and smeared the blood on to a microscope slide. The smear was stained with a special dye.

4(a) Why was the skin wiped with cotton wool and alcohol? *(1)*
 (b) Why was the needle sterile? *(1)*
5 When you look at a red blood cell under a light microscope, the central part looks paler. Why is this? *(2)*
6 A drop of blood was placed on a slide and mixed with distilled water. Explain what would happen. *(2)*

Total 15 marks

30 Ribs and diaphragm

The diagram below shows part of the human skeleton in the region of the chest.

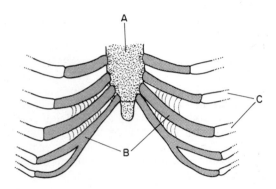

1(a) What are the structures labelled B? *(1)*
 (b) Why do the structures labelled B need to be flexible? *(1)*
2(a) When you breathe in, in what directions do the ribs move? *(2)*
 (b) What makes the ribs move? *(1)*
3(a) Describe carefully the position of the diaphragm. *(1)*
 (b) How does the shape of the diaphragm change as you breathe in? *(1)*
 (c) Explain how the movement of the ribs and diaphragm during breathing in, changes the volume and pressure within the chest. *(3)*

A sample of exhaled air was analysed. The results are shown below.
Original volume of air   = 10.0 cm³
Volume of air after treatment with potassium hydroxide = 9.6 cm³
Volume of air after treatment with potassium pyrogallate = 8.0 cm³

4(a) Assuming that the sample consists only of carbon dioxide, oxygen and nitrogen, what was the percentage of
 (i) carbon dioxide
 (ii) oxygen
 (iii) nitrogen? *(3)*
 (b) List two ways in which inspired and expired air differ. *(2)*

Total 15 marks

31 Bronchitis

1   Copy and complete the following pathway of inhaled air from the nose to the lungs.
     Nasal cavities → A → bronchus → B → air sacs in lungs   (2)
2   Give one reason why it is better to breathe through the nose than the mouth.   (1)

Chronic bronchitis kills many people each year. It is caused by repeated irritation of the lining of the air passages of the lungs. Smoke, dust, fumes and sulphur dioxide help cause this disease. The disease is common in all industrialised countries. A patient with bronchitis coughs up mucus, tends to wheeze and quickly 'runs out of breath'. Air sacs in the lungs are damaged and the lungs lose their elasticity. Also, the damage to the blood circulation in the lungs puts an additional strain on the right hand side of the heart. This can lead to heart failure.

3   Give one industry whose workers would be likely to develop chronic bronchitis.   (1)
4(a) Why are the lungs elastic?   (1)
 (b) What will be the effect of the loss of the air sacs on the amount of oxygen carried by the blood?   (2)
5   A high level of sulphur dioxide (and other acidic gases) in the atmosphere increases the risk of developing chronic bronchitis. Where does most of the sulphur dioxide come from?   (2)

In 1956, the Clean Air Act was passed by Parliament. This reduced the amount of smoke that was allowed out of factory chimneys and the local authorities were able to introduce smokeless zones.

6   Explain what effect you think this may have had on the level of bronchitis in this country?   (2)
7(a) People who smoke are more likely to develop bronchitis. Explain why you think this happens.   (2)
 (b) In a healthy person, how are the lungs kept clean?   (2)

Total 15 marks

32 Smoking

The equipment shown below can be used to show some of the effects of cigarette smoking. The equipment can be made to 'smoke' by opening and closing tube A with a finger. Smoke contains tar, nicotine, carbon monoxide and carbon dioxide.

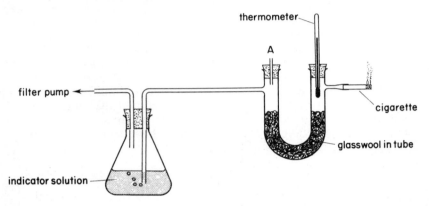

1(a) Why is the machine attached to a pump? *(1)*
 (b) What would you expect to happen to the glass wool? *(1)*
2   How could you use this apparatus to compare tipped and untipped cigarettes? *(4)*
3(a) Carbon monoxide from the smoke in cigarettes can combine with the haemoglobin in red blood cells. This is irreversible. What will the effect of this be on the oxygen carrying capacity of the blood? *(1)*
 (b) Give two other harmful effects of cigarette smoking. *(2)*

The figures in the table below show the amount of tobacco smoked in Britain until 1975 in the form of cigarettes.

| | Amount of tobacco smoked (in grams) per adult per day | |
Year	Men	Women
1900	0.8	0
1925	6.0	0.25
1950	9.0	2.75
1975	10.0	7.0

4 What conclusions can you draw from the table about smoking in men and women? (2)

The table below shows the mass of babies born to smoking and non-smoking mothers.

Birth weight (kg)	Mother non-smoker % all births	Mother smoker % all births
less than 2.0	2.6	3.3
2.1 to 3.0	10.9	22.5
3.1 to 4.0	44.9	45.0
4.1 to 5.0	26.7	22.5
5.1+	14.9	6.7

5 What percentage of
  (i) smokers' babies
  (ii) non-smokers' babies
had a birth weight of less than 3.0 kg? (2)
6 What seems to be the effect of smoking during pregnancy on the development of the baby? (1)
7 Suggest two other factors which might affect the birth weight of the baby. (2)

Babies that weight less than 2 kg at birth have problems. They appear rather red and wrinkled and the skin has no fat. They are liable to get infections and may have problems with breathing and temperature regulation.

8 Why do low birth weight babies have greater problems with temperature regulation than normal babies? (2)
9 Bearing in mind your answer to question 4, do you think that the number of low birth weight babies is increasing or decreasing? Explain your reasoning. (2)

Total 20 marks

33 Olympic performance

When running a short race, the body gains most of its energy from anaerobic respiration (respiration without oxygen). This energy is gained by breaking down sugar to lactic acid and carbon dioxide. This cannot go on for long as the body cannot tolerate high levels of lactic acid. Afterwards, extra oxygen must be supplied to the body to 'burn off' this lactic acid.

1   Write the equation (in words) for anaerobic respiration.   *(1)*

2(a) Give one effect that a build-up of lactic acid would have on
       a runner.   *(1)*

  (b) Suggest two ways in which the body can increase the
       amount of oxygen taken in by the lungs.   *(2)*

On a longer race, some aerobic respiration must take place. Therefore a long distance runner must be able to supply more oxygen to the muscles to make sure that more of the sugar is completely broken down to carbon dioxide and water.

3   Write the equation (in words) for aerobic respiration   *(1)*

The figures below show the winning times for some races at different distances for the Rome and Mexico City Olympics.

| | | *Time(s)* |
Distance (m)	Rome 1960	Mexico City 1968
100	10.2	9.9
200	20.5	19.8
5000	823.4	868.4
10 000	1712.2	1767.4

4   How much faster or slower in 1968 was the
       (i) 100 m
      (ii) 200 m
     (iii) 5000 m
     (iv) 10 000 m?   *(4)*

Mexico City is over 2000 m above sea level. Atmospheric pressure falls with altitude.

5(a) How will high altitude affect the amount of oxygen that can be supplied to the cells? *(1)*
 (b) In which races do you think high altitude affected the winning times at Mexico City? *(2)*
 (c) How can you explain your answer to (b)? *(2)*

People who live at high altitudes all the time show the following changes in their bodies:
(a)   they breathe deeply
(b)   their blood volume increases from 5 to 6.5 litres
(c)   the number of red blood cells in their blood increases from 5 to 7 million per cm^3.

6   Carefully explain what effect each of these changes will have on the amount of oxygen in the blood. *(3)*
7   Explain why athletes who were born and lived at high altitudes were at an advantage in the Mexico Games compared to those who lived at or near sea level. *(1)*
8   When athletes run a marathon (26 miles), what other problems might they face? *(2)*

Total 20 marks

34 Kidney function

Three test tubes were set up as follows:

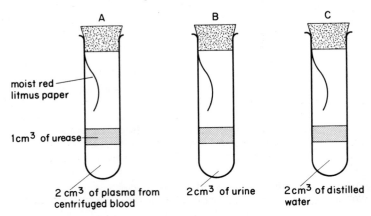

The enzyme urease breaks down urea to release ammonia. The presence of ammonia can be detected by its effect on moist red litmus paper. The tubes were incubated at 37 °C for one hour. At the end of the hour, the colour of the litmus paper was recorded and the contents of each tube were tested with Benedict's solution and Biuret reagents. The results are shown below.

Test	A	B	C
Litmus	Turns blue	Turns blue	No change
Benedict's	Turns orange	No change	No change
Biuret	Turns violet	No change	No change

1 Using the results, what is the substance that the tests show is present in the plasma and the urine? *(1)*
2 Why were the tubes incubated at 37 °C? *(1)*
3 Name one substance that is present in all three tubes. *(1)*
4(a) From the results of the experiment, what substances are found in blood plasma but not in urine or distilled water? *(2)*
 (b) Why are these not lost from the body? *(2)*
5 What is the purpose of tube C? *(1)*

The diagram below shows the basis of an artificial kidney machine.

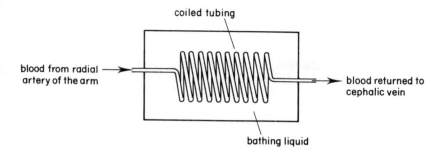

coiled tubing

blood from radial artery of the arm

blood returned to cephalic vein

bathing liquid

The blood from a patient flows through a tube made of a partially permeable membrane which is similar to visking (dialysis) tubing. This allows some substances to pass through it but not others. Dialysing fluid, which consists largely of potassium chloride, magnesium chloride and sodium ethanoate, flows round it.

6 Why is the tube coiled rather than straight? *(1)*

7 Which of the following could pass through the membrane?
  proteins, red blood cells, urea, ammonia *(2)*

8 The venous tube leading from the dialysis tube is narrower than the arterial one. What is the effect of this? *(2)*

9 If someone is being kept on renal dialysis which foodstuffs must be restricted in their diet? *(2)*

Total 15 marks

35 The effect of alcohol

Alcohol is a powerful drug. It affects the central nervous system, slowing down many reflex reactions. Vision and speech may also be impaired. The small blood vessels in the skin dilate. About 20% of the alcohol drunk is absorbed through the wall of the stomach, the rest through the intestine. Most of it is broken down to water and carbon dioxide, though some is lost by the lungs and in sweat. A volunteer was give three large vodkas. Blood samples (for analysis) were withdrawn from a vein over the next five hours. The table below shows how much alcohol was found in the blood.

Time since drinking (hours)	0	0.5	1.0	1.5	2.0	3.0	4.0	5.0
mg alcohol per 100 cm^3 blood	0	70	140	150	110	70	50	40

1 Use these figures to plot a graph. (5)
2 Use your graph to answer the following questions.
 (a) How many milligrams of alcohol would you expect to find in the blood after 2.5 hours? (1)
 (b) The legal limit for driving is 80 mg alcohol per 100 cm^3. For how long would the volunteer be above the limit? (2)
3(a) What would be one effect of the dilation of the small blood vessels in the skin? (1)
 (b) Why does alcohol affect muscular response? (2)
 (c) The body breaks down most of the alcohol to carbon dioxide and water. How may these be lost from the body? (2)

Chronic alcohol abuse often leads to malnutrition and to vitamin deficiency as the alcoholic rejects food. Deficiency of the B vitamins is a common feature of alcoholism.

5 What does the term 'malnutrition' mean? (1)
6 What disease or symptoms would arise in a person with a named B vitamin deficiency? (1)

Total 15 marks

36 The skin

The outer layer of the skin of a mammal consists of dead cells. The table below shows how its thickness varies over the body.

Body site	Thickness (μm)
Head	50
Arms and legs	60
Fingers	220
Fingertips	370
Sole of foot	1050

1 How does this layer help to protect the body? *(2)*
2(a) What are the advantages of having thicker skin on the
    (i) finger tips
    (ii) soles of the feet? *(2)*
 (b) Why is the epidermis thinnest on the head? *(1)*
3 Apart from its protective function, the skin helps to maintain a constant body temperature. Explain how the hairs, moved by erector muscles, can help to maintain body temperature on a cold day. *(2)*
4(a) A man digging a garden produces 2 litres of sweat. If it takes 2.5 kJ to evaporate 1 cm³ of water, how much heat energy must be taken from his body to evaporate the sweat? *(1)*
 (b) If his daily energy intake (as food) was 18 000 kJ, calculate what percentage of this energy was lost in the evaporation of water. *(2)*
5 Name one area of the skin surface that has no sweat glands. *(1)*

Animals that live in deserts often have to face extremes of temperature, from 70 °C to 80 °C during the day and near zero at night. The horned lizard which is found in the Mexican desert turns a pale colour in the heat of the sun and may pant.

6 Explain how
    (i) changing to a paler colour
    (ii) panting
    help the lizard from becoming too hot. *(4)*

Total 15 marks

37 Human body temperature

In a healthy person, body temperature does not vary very much
during a day. Maintaining a steady body temperature, of about
37 °C, is very important. Old people and babies are not so good at
controlling their body temperature and this is why it is important
that they are kept warm. The graph below shows how an adult's
body temperature changes during the day. The temperature was
recorded in two ways:

(a) by using a thermometer in the mouth – *oral* temperature.
(b) by inserting a thermometer in the rectum to give the *rectal*
or *deep body* temperature.

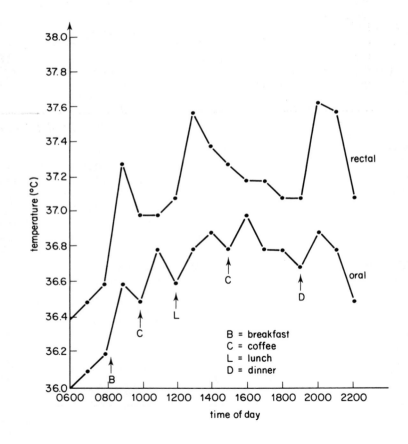

Use the graph to answer the following questions.

1(a) What were the lowest temperatures recorded
    (i) orally
    (ii) rectally?   (2)
 (b) What were the highest temperatures recorded
    (i) orally
    (ii) rectally?   (2)

2(a) At what period of the day were the oral and rectal
    temperatures at their lowest?   (1)
 (b) Suggest one reason why temperatures are at their lowest
    during this period.   (1)

3   The body temperature increased during the course of the
    day. Give one reason for this.   (1)

4(a) What effect did morning coffee have on the oral and rectal
    temperatures?   (2)
 (b) Why did the body temperature rise after meals?   (2)

5   Why does the oral temperature vary more than the rectal
    temperature?   (2)

6(a) Elderly people in particular lose heat very easily. They can
    lose too much and die. What is the condition called where
    the body temperature falls dangerously low?   (1)
 (b) Premature babies are usually put in an incubator. What is
    the reason for this?   (1)

Total 15 marks

38 The eye

Animals do not all have their eyes in the same position on their heads. Where their eyes are is important for how they live. The diagrams below show the field of view for two different positions of the eyes.

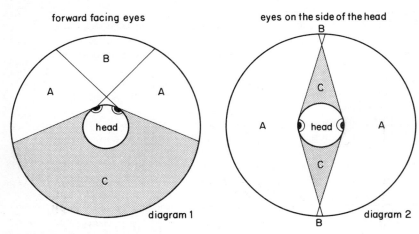

forward facing eyes   eyes on the side of the head

diagram 1   diagram 2

A = the field of view for one eye only
B = the field of view covered by both eyes
C = where neither eye can see

1   What is meant by the term 'field of view'?   (1)
2(a) Give one example of an animal with eyes which face
     forward as in diagram 1.   (1)
 (b) What is this sort of vision called?   (1)
 (c) Give one advantage of having forward facing eyes. Explain
     why this is important for the way the animal lives.   (2)
3(a) Give one example of an animal with eyes on the sides of the
     head as in diagram 2.   (1)
 (b) Give one advantage of having eyes on the side of the head.
     Explain why this is important for the way the animal lives.   (2)
4   In some grazing animals like zebras, the eyeball is adapted
    so that both near and far away objects can be brought into
    focus on the retina at the same time. How is this an
    advantage to animals like the zebra?   (2)

Total 10 marks

39 Nerve cells and reflex arcs

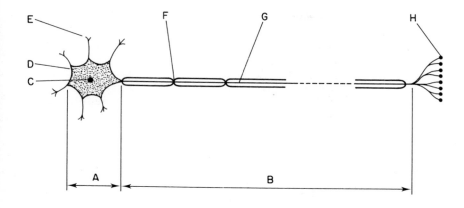

1 Study the diagram above of a motor neuron (nerve cell).
   Using the letters A–H, match them to the statements below.
   You may use each letter as often as you like or not at all.
    (i) The part that forms the most of the grey matter.
   (ii) The part that directly stimulates a muscle.
   (iii) A part rich in DNA.
   (iv) The part that receives electrical signals.
   (v) The part surrounded by a fatty myelin sheath.   (5)

If you touch something very hot, your hand jerks away. This
happens without you having to think about it. It is an example of a
reflex action.

2(a) Name one simple reflex action involving a sense organ in
     the head and state its function.   (2)
  (b) Draw a simple diagram to show a named reflex action. On
     your diagram, label the sensory neuron (nerve cell), motor
     neuron, effector (muscle) and spinal cord. Show the
     direction of the electrical (nerve) impulse.   (6)
  (c) Give two reasons why it is important for animals to have
     reflex actions.   (2)

Total 15 marks

40 Response of plants to stimuli

Some wheat seeds were planted in three seed trays and allowed to germinate. When young shoots appeared above soil level, all round lighting was given for three days. At the end of this time, the three trays received different treatments.

tray 1: the shoots were left lit from all sides.
tray 2: the shoots were lit from one side only.
tray 3: the tips of the shoots were covered with aluminium foil and also lit from one side only.

Diagram 1 below shows the effects of these different treatments.

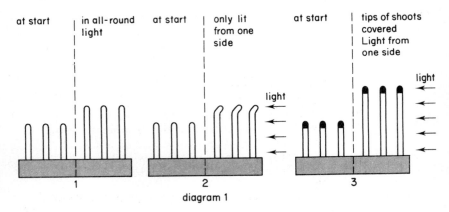

diagram 1

1(a) Measure the original and final lengths of the stems (to the nearest mm) in the three trays and calculate the percentage change in length of the stems. *(3)*
(b) Which tray of stems has grown the most? *(1)*
(c) Why was it important to include tray 1 as part of the experiment? *(2)*
(d) State three conclusions that may be drawn from this investigation. *(3)*
(e) Seedlings growing in the shade of a much larger plant may survive because of their ability to respond to light. Explain how a seedling's ability to respond to light increases its chance of survival. *(2)*

Diagram 2 below shows a bean seed germinating whilst suspended in a glass tank. The tank was lit from all sides evenly. Diagram 3 shows the appearance of the seedling 3 days later.

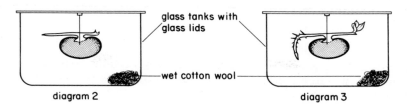

glass tanks with glass lids

wet cotton wool

diagram 2   diagram 3

2(a) Why was the wet cotton wool placed in the tank?   (1)
 (b) To what stimulus do you think the root and shoot were
     responding?   (1)
 (c) Explain your reasoning.   (2)

Diagram 4 is an enlarged view of the seedling after 3 days.

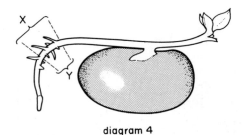

X

Y

diagram 4

3(a) What must have happened to the cells in region X compared
     to those in region Y?   (1)
 (b) What chemical might be responsible for the changes seen?   (1)
 (c) How does the response of the lateral roots differ in this
     experiment from the response of the main root?   (1)
 (d) How might this difference in response of the lateral roots
     benefit the seedling if it were growing in soil?   (2)

Total 20 marks

41 Osmosis

Osmosis is the passage of water molecules from a dilute solution through a selectively permeable membrane to a more concentrated solution.

1(a) What is meant by the term 'selectively permeable'? (*1*)
 (b) Give an example of a selectively permeable membrane
    found in the body. (*1*)

An experiment to demonstrate osmosis was set up as below.

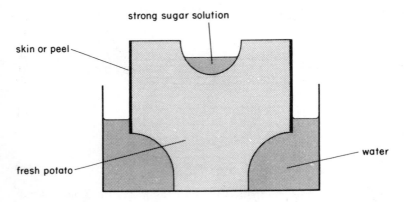

strong sugar solution

skin or peel

water

fresh potato

2(a) Explain with the help of a diagram what you would expect
    to happen after 2 hours. (*3*)
 (b) How would the result have been different if boiled potato
    tissue had been used? (*1*)
 (c) What effect would boiling have had on the selectively
    permeable membranes? (*2*)

In another experiment to demonstrate osmosis a freshly cut dandelion stem was cut into four equal vertical sections. The four sections were treated as follows:
    Section A – placed in water.
    Section B – placed in concentrated sugar solution.
    Section C – placed in dilute sugar solution.
    Section D – left exposed to the air on the bench.
The diagram below shows the experiment and how sections A and B looked after 20 minutes. The heavily shaded areas on the segments represent the water-proof epidermis.

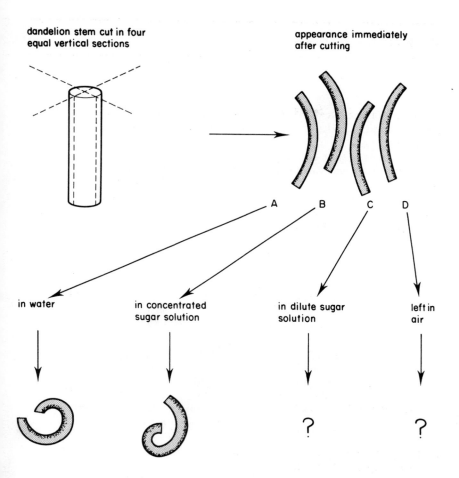

dandelion stem cut in four equal vertical sections

appearance immediately after cutting

A B C D

in water

in concentrated sugar solution

in dilute sugar solution

left in air

appearance after 20 minutes

3   Explain the appearance of strips A and B. (4)
4   Draw diagrams to show what you would expect to happen to strips C and D. (2)
5   Explain the appearance of strips C and D. (4)
6   Why did all the pieces of the stem curl slightly immediately after cutting? (2)

Total 20 marks

42 Plants and water

An experiment was done to measure the transpiration rate of a potted plant.

1(a) What is meant by the term transpiration? *(1)*
  (b) State two ways in which transpiration benefits a plant. *(2)*

The pot and the lower part of the stem where there were no leaves were put inside a plastic bag. The bag was then firmly sealed around the stem. The potted plant was weighed by placing it on top of a balance. The mass was read straight away. The apparatus was then left for eight hours near a window in a brightly lit laboratory. The results were:

Reading at the start of the experiment   = 1986 g
Reading after eight hours   = 1930 g

2(a) What was the average loss of water from the plant in grams per hour? *(2)*
  (b) Why was the pot sealed in a polythene bag? *(1)*
  (c) If the experiment was done on a dull, humid day in what way would the results have been different? Give the reason for your answer. *(2)*
  (d) If the lower surface of the leaves was coated with Vaseline, what effect would you expect it to have on the rate of transpiration? *(2)*
3(a) Plants take up water through their root surface. What part of the root increases this surface area for water uptake? *(1)*
  (b) How does water enter the cells of the root? *(1)*
  (c) Once inside the plant, water moves from the roots to the leaves through the xylem. Describe a simple experiment to show this. *(3)*

Total 15 marks

43 Photosynthesis and gas exchange

Plants such as privet may have three different types of leaves on the plant. They may be all green, green with a white area or all white. Various leaves of similar age and surface area were taken from a destarched plant and used in the experiment shown below. Each leaf was suspended in a tube so that it did not fall into the bicarbonate indicator solution.

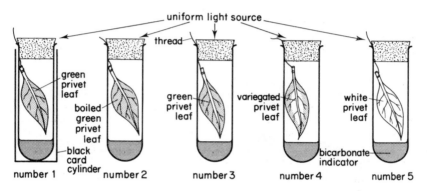

Note: 5 cm³ hydrogen carbonate (bicarbonate) indicator was placed in each test tube with each leaf. The tubes were sealed with rubber bungs.

1(a) Why did the leaves have to be of similar age and surface area? (1)
 (b) Why was each leaf suspended by a cotton thread? (1)
2   How would you destarch a leaf? (1)
3   The indicator turns yellow if the solution is acid and purple if it is alkaline. Which gas produced by the activities of the leaf would cause the indicator to turn yellow? (1)
4(a) Give one way in which the design of the experiment could be improved. (1)
 (b) How would this decrease the risk of experimental error? (1)
5(a) In which tube(s) does photosynthesis occur? (2)
 (b) In which tube(s) does respiration occur? (4)
 (c) In which tube(s) would the indicator quickly change to purple? (1)
 (d) In which tube(s) does the indicator change to yellow? (2)

Total 15 marks

44 Photosynthesis and light intensity

The rate of photosynthesis of Canadian pondweed was measured. The pond weed was placed under an inverted funnel in a beaker. A test-tube filled with water was placed over the end of the funnel. The rate was measured by counting the number of bubbles released into the test tube every 5 minutes. The apparatus was kept at 20 °C and different light intensities used. The results obtained are shown in the table below.

Light intensity (arbitrary units)	Rate of photosynthesis (bubbles per 5 minute period)
0	0
10	7
20	14
30	22
40	29
50	38
60	43
70	45

1   Draw a diagram of the apparatus used to collect the bubbles.   (*3*)

2(a) Plot a graph of the results in the table.   (*5*)

  (b) Use your graph to find the number of gas bubbles given off in a five minute period at a light intensity of 25 units.   (*1*)

  (c) Describe the relationship between the level of photosynthesis and light intensity up to 50 units of light.   (*1*)

  (d) If the light intensity was increased beyond 75 light units, suggest what might happen to the rate of photosynthesis.   (*1*)

  (e) Explain what would happen if the experiment was repeated at 30 °C.   (*2*)

3(a) Suggest two ways in which the gas collected in the test tube might differ from normal atmospheric air.   (*2*)

  (b) What assumptions have you made about bubble size?   (*1*)

  (c) How could you adapt the experiment to make it more accurate?   (*2*)

4   Give two reasons why pond weeds are important in a pond.   (*2*)

Total 20 marks

45 Photosynthesis and chlorophyll

Spirogyra is a filamentous green alga. It has large cells and each of these has a ribbon-like chloroplast which runs round the edge of the cell. The diagram below shows the result of an experiment using this alga. Light which had passed through a prism was shone at the filament of cells. In the water around the algal cells were many bacteria. When the alga started to photosynthesise, the bacteria moved to those areas where there was plenty of oxygen. Before the experiment, the alga and the bacteria were kept in the dark.

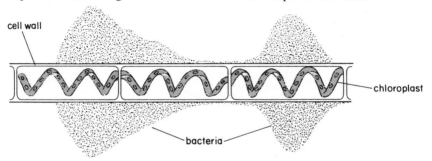

cell wall

chloroplast

bacteria

violet   blue   indigo   green   yellow   orange   red   colour of light

1   How does oxygen pass from the alga to the surrounding
    water?   (1)
2   Why was it important to use bacteria that could move in this
    experiment?   (1)
3   For what process do the bacteria need oxygen?   (1)
4   Which colours of light were most effective in photosynthesis? (1)
5   Give two sources of the carbon dioxide for the alga.   (2)
6   Why were the alga and bacteria kept in the dark before the
    start of the experiment?   (2)

It is possible to find out which colours (wavelengths) of light are absorbed by chlorophyll. This can be done by shining a beam of light through a solution of extracted chlorophyll. As the light emerges from the solution, it is passed through a prism and projected onto a screen. When this is done, it is found that the red and blue light are missing.

7   How does this help explain the first set of results?   (2)

Total 10 marks

46 The menstrual cycle and conception

The graph below shows how the lining of the uterus changes during the menstrual cycle.

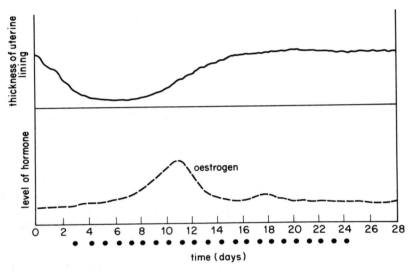

• indicates day on which the pill should be taken

1(a) Copy the graph above and mark on it a line to show how the level of progesterone changes during the cycle. (3)
 (b) Where is progesterone produced? (1)
2(a) On your graph, mark the days you would expect menstruation (bleeding) to occur with the letter M. (1)
 (b) On your graph, mark with the letter O the day on which you would expect ovulation (egg release) to take place. (1)
3 What is the name given to the stage in a girl's life when menstruation usually starts? (1)
4 Some women have symptoms such as sickness, tiredness and irritability a few days before menstruation starts each month. What is the name given to this condition? (1)
5 The recommended daily intake of iron is 10 mg for a man and 12 mg for a woman. Bearing in mind the loss of blood during menstruation, how can you explain the difference. (2)

At ovulation, an egg is released from an ovary. The egg travels along the fallopian tube to the uterus.

6 Why are the fallopian tubes lined with cilia (tiny hairs)? *(1)*

If sexual intercourse takes place the egg may become fertilised by a sperm. The nuclei of the egg and sperm fuse and the embryo is formed. A human cell usually contains 46 chromosomes. This is the diploid number. The gametes are haploid and each contain 23 chromosomes.

7 How many chromosomes are there in
  (i) a human egg
  (ii) a human sperm
  (iii) the zygote? *(3)*

If a woman does not want to become pregnant she can take the contraceptive pill. This has to be done on the days shown on the graph.

8(a) When does she take the first pill? *(1)*
  (b) How many days after she takes the last pill does the next period begin? *(1)*
9 A couple are not using any form of contraception. If intercourse takes place on day 24, could the woman become pregnant? Explain your answer. *(2)*

As a woman reaches the age of 40–50, her menstrual cycle usually becomes irregular.

10(a) What is this stage called? *(1)*
  (b) Apart from her menstrual cycle becoming irregular, what other symptoms may she have? *(1)*

Total 20 marks

47 Human foetal growth

The table below shows the changes in size of a human foetus.

Length of gestation (weeks)	5	6	7	9	11	12	16	20	24	28	32	36	40
Length (mm)	2	6	13	30	55	90	180	250	330	380	430	460	508
Mass (g)	–	–	–	2	10	14	113	340	623	907	1800	2380	3180

1(a) Plot a graph of the data in the table. (6)
 (b) Use your graph to estimate
    (i) the length
    (ii) the mass
   of the foetus at 30 weeks gestation. (2)
 (c) What was the percentage increase in
    (i) the length
    (ii) the mass
   between weeks 36 and 40? (2)

Soon after the embryo becomes embedded in the wall of the uterus, a placenta forms. This brings the blood vessels of the mother and the foetus very close together to allow substances to pass between them. However, the blood of the embryo and mother do not mix or come into direct contact.

2 Give two reasons why it is important for the survival of the embryo that the two blood systems do not mix. (2)
3(a) Name one waste material that has to pass from the foetus to the mother. (1)
 (b) What will happen to this substance after it has passed into the mother's blood? (2)
4(a) Name two substances that must pass from the mother to the foetus and briefly explain why they are needed. (3)
 (b) Pregnant women are usually advised not to smoke or take any drugs during pregnancy. Explain why. (2)

Total 20 marks

48 The growth and development of a child

In 1759 Count Philibert de Montbeillard had a son. The Count measured his son's height until 1777, when the boy was 18. The measurements recorded by the Count are shown below.

Time (years)	birth	2	4	6	8	10	12	14	16	18
Height (cm)	50	90	105	118	130	143	150	164	180	183

1(a) How much did the Count's son grow between
  (i) birth and 2 years
  (ii) 4 and 6 years
  (iii) 10 and 12 years
  (iv) 14 and 16 years? *(4)*
 (b) In which two year period was growth fastest? *(1)*
2(a) Suggest three changes that would have happened to the boy's body between 14 and 18 years. *(3)*
 (b) The hormone testosterone is largely responsible for these changes. Where in the body is it produced? *(1)*
3(a) Suggest two other factors which might have affected the boy's growth. Explain how they have their effect. *(4)*
 (b) How else could the Count have measured the growth of his son? *(1)*
4(a) Growth requires the formation of new cells. What is the name of the type of cell division which produces genetically identical daughter cells? *(1)*
 (b) Name two areas or parts of the body where this type of cell division is always occurring. *(2)*
5 If the boy was the son of a French peasant rather than of a count would you expect him to have grown as fast or as tall? Explain your answer. *(2)*

Nowadays, the most common causes of death in Europe and the United States are heart disease or cancer. In the 1700's the most common causes of death were infectious diseases.

6 Give one reason why infectious diseases are no longer the most common cause of death in Europe and the United States. *(1)*

Total 20 marks

49 Human population growth ✓

The table below shows the population for the European and African continents since 1650.

Year		1650	1750	1800	1850	1900	1930	1950	1968
Population (millions)	Europe	100	140	187	266	401	534	572	695
	Africa	100	95	90	95	120	164	222	332

1 Use the data to plot a graph of the population growth of Europe and Africa from 1650 to 1968. *(6)*

2(a) Give one similarity between the two graphs. *(1)*

(b) Give one difference between the two graphs. *(1)*

(c) Suggest a reason why the population of Africa fell in the 1700's and 1800's. *(1)*

3(a) What was the percentage increase between 1850 and 1950 in the

(i) European population.

(ii) African population. *(2)*

(b) What was the percentage increase between 1950 and 1968 in the

(i) European population

(ii) African population? *(2)*

4 Disease, famine, war and natural disasters are all important events in the growth of human populations. Explain how these have influenced the populations of Africa and Europe in the last 100 years. *(4)*

The table below shows the change in the average age at which people died in Europe since 1650.

Year	1650	1750	1881	1921	1940	1950	1967
Age	27	40	45	57	63	67	72

5 What is the relationship between these figures and your answer to question 4? *(3)*

Total 20 marks

50 Populations and life expectancy

The table below gives some data about the population of the United Kingdom in 1901 and the estimated population in 2001.

Ages	1901 Number in millions	2001 Number in millions
0–14	12.4	11.8
15–29	10.8	10.6
30–44	7.5	13.0
45–59	4.6	10.9
60–74	2.4	7.4
75+	0.5	4.0

1(a) What was the total population in 1901? *(1)*
 (b) What is the total population predicted for 2001? *(1)*
2   Draw a histogram to compare the age structures of the populations in 1901 and 2001. *(5)*
3(a) What percentage of the population was over 60 in 1901? *(1)*
 (b) What percentage of the population is expected to be over 60 in 2001? *(1)*
 (c) What problems would be associated with a population with a larger percentage of population over 60? *(2)*
 (d) Give two reasons why we seem to be living longer nowadays. *(2)*
4(a) The 1984 census revealed that 11.7 million people were aged 60 or over. Of these 6.8 million were women. What percentage of the population over 60 were women? *(1)*
 (b) What explanation can you offer for this? *(1)*

Total 15 marks

51 Contraception ✓

Gossypol is a chemical which can be extracted from the seeds of cotton plants. When it was fed to rats, mice, dogs and monkeys, it caused a reduction in the fertility of the male animals. This led to the idea that it could be used as a human male contraceptive. An investigation was carried out on 9000 male volunteers. Before the start of the investigation, the sperm count of each volunteer was checked. A sperm count between 40 and 250 million sperm per cm^3 is normal and likely to result in fertilisation. When given the gossypol, over 99% of the men showed a massive reduction in their sperm count, down to 4 million sperm per cm^3. But while they were taking gossypol, a number of the men reported various side effects.

  1080 suffered from fatigue
  630 suffered from stomach and intestinal upsets
  540 suffered from reduced sex drive
  66 suffered from extreme potassium loss and needed to be
      admitted to hospital.

In a follow-up study some 6 months later, when the men had ceased taking the gossypol, it was found that 25% of them still had a reduced sperm count.

1 Why was the sperm count of the men checked before they
   started to take the gossypol?   (1)
2 Assuming that no man reported more than one side effect,
   what percentage of the men suffered a side effect whilst
   taking the chemical?   (1)
3 Why is a high sperm count needed for fertilisation?   (1)
4 What do you consider to be the most serious problem in
   using gossypol as a male contraceptive?   (1)

There are several different methods of preventing pregnancy. The cap (diaphragm) and sheath (condom) are termed *barrier methods* because an actual barrier is used to prevent pregnancy. The coil or intra uterine device (IUD) is fitted by a doctor and may be left in place for several years. The pill (oral contraceptive) is a hormonal method of birth control. Sterilisation usually involves cutting or tying the tubes to prevent the egg and sperm meeting. This is a permanent method of contraception and is not easily reversed.

5 Use the words in the list below to answer the following questions. You may use each word once, more than once or not at all.

uterus, fallopian tubes (oviducts), sperm duct, prostate gland, ovary, testis, vagina, cervix, vasectomy,

(i) Which structure(s) produce the eggs?
(ii) Which structure(s) would be cut to stop eggs reaching the womb?
(iii) Where would the coil (IUD) be placed?.
(iv) Which structure must the cap (diaphragm) cover completely to prevent pregnancy?
(v) What is male sterilisation called? *(5)*

6 The sheath and the cap can be made more effective in preventing pregnancy if a spermicidal foam or jelly is also used during intercourse. Why do you think this is more effective? *(1)*

7 Sterilisation is not always successful in preventing pregnancy. Suggest why it sometimes fails. *(2)*

8 Many women have decided to stop taking the pill because of recent reports about possible side effects. Name two side effects the pill is thought to have. *(2)*

Some people prefer not to use artificial methods of birth control. To avoid pregnancy they use the rhythm method or safe period. Women who use this method may use two ways to work out when it is safe to have intercourse and avoid pregnancy. The first is by taking the woman's temperature every day, as this rises noticeably when she ovulates. The second is by working out the length of her menstrual cycle, so that she can work out the day on which she is most likely to ovulate. Despite taking these measurements, the rhythm method is only 76% successful in preventing pregnancy.

9(a) Assuming a cycle of 28 days, on what day would an egg normally be released? *(1)*
  (b) Give one reason why the rhythm method is not always successful. *(1)*

The sheath is recommended as a way to stop the spread of sexually transmitted diseases.

10(a) Name two diseases spread by sexual contact. *(2)*
   (b) Explain how the sheath can protect both partners. *(2)*

Total 20 marks

52 Triplets

Human body cells usually contain 23 pairs of chromosomes. The exception to this rule is the cells that form the gametes.

1(a) Copy and complete the table below.

	Total number of chromosomes	Type of sex chromosomes present
Female body cells		
Male body cells		
Spermatozoa		
Eggs/ova		

(4)

(b) What is the name given to the type of cell division that produces the sperm and the eggs? (1)

(c) Where in the
  (i) male body
  (ii) female body
does this type of cell division occur? (2)

2   Explain how identical twins may arise. (2)

In 1967, a set of triplets was born, but their mother died. They were separated at a very young age and brought up under very different circumstances. When they were 19 they met for the first time since their separation. A doctor who was interested in triplets recorded the following information about them.

	James	Thomas	Richard
Height (cm)	187	187.5	179
Mass	80	86	96
Blood group	O	AB	O
Intelligence quotient	137	140	127

3(a) Which two of the boys might be identical twins on the evidence available? (1)

(b) Explain which piece of evidence is most important in answering this question. (1)

The ABO blood group is determined by three genes or alleles, I^A and I^B which are dominant, and i which is recessive.

Genotype		Phenotype i.e. Blood group
$I^A I^A$	→	A
$I^A i$	→	A
$I^B I^B$	→	B
$I^B i$	→	B
$I^A I^B$	→	AB
i i	→	O

4 Using this information, work out the genotypes of the parents of the triplets. Show clearly how you arrive at your answer. (5)

All the boys had straight hair, but a photograph of their parents showed that both their father and mother had wavy hair. The gene for wavy hair is dominant to straight. Using the symbols H for the dominant gene and h for the recessive gene answer the following questions.

5(a) What genotype do the boys have? (1)
(b) Explain how the boys can have straight hair even though their parents had wavy hair. (3)

Total 20 marks

53 Human genetic disorders

Huntingdon's Chorea is a fatal disease of the brain but it does not normally appear until middle age. Death then follows within a few years. The diagram below shows an affected family. The father, who was heterozygous for the condition, died of the disease 4 years ago when he was 43.

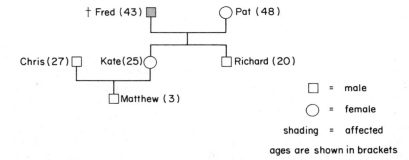

1(a) Using the symbols H for chorea and h for the normal gene, what is Pat's genotype? (1)
  (b) What are chances (probability) that Kate will develop the disease? Explain your answer. (2)
2(a) What do you understand by the term 'genetic counselling'? (2)
  (b) What advice would you give Richard (and his wife) about having children? (1)

Cystic fibrosis is an inherited disorder which affects sweat and mucus production in the body. The mucus produced is very sticky. This causes blockages of the small air passages in the lungs and also of the pancreatic duct. About 1 child in 2000 is affected by this condition. It is due to a recessive gene.

3(a) The lungs cannot easily remove this sticky mucus. What effect do you think this will have? (2)
  (b) If the fat and protein digesting enzymes of the pancreas cannot reach the intestine, what effect will this have on the growth and development of an affected individual? (2)

The diagram below shows a family tree.

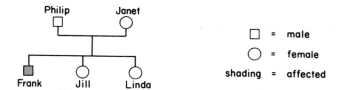

2 Using the symbols, F for the dominant gene and f for the recessive:

(a) give the genotypes (genetic make-up) of the parents. *(2)*

(b) give the genotypes of Frank, Jill and Linda. Show clearly how you arrive at your answers. *(3)*

(c) if the parents decide to have another child, what is the chance (probability) that it too will be affected? *(1)*

Sometimes people of normal height have children with the condition called *Achondroplasia*. A mutation must therefore occur either in the production of the sperm or eggs. When fully grown, people with achondroplasia are very short, thick-set individuals with rather large squarish heads. The upper part of the arms and legs is particularly short. Their intelligence and mental capacities are quite normal. The pelvis is also affected. Its width is normal but its depth (from front and to back) is reduced. Therefore women with this condition have difficulty giving birth, and children are usually born by Caesarian section. A family tree, where the mutation has occurred, is shown below:

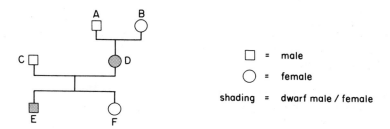

5 Which of the individuals (A–F) are

(i) normal females?

(ii) dwarf males? *(3)*

6(a) What is a Caesarian section? *(1)*

(b) Why do you think that dwarf women find childbirth difficult? *(2)*

7 Do you think the mutation is dominant or recessive? Explain your answer. *(3)*

Total 25 marks

54 Radiation and life

Radiation may cause permanent changes in the genetic material which is inherited.

1 What term is used to describe an inherited change in the genetic material? *(1)*

It may also cause changes in the cell machinery so that cells become cancerous. That is they grow at an uncontrolled rate within the body. This was first seen in Austrian miners from Schneeberg and Jachymow. The mines in these areas have been worked for hundreds of years and are rich in radioactive ores. Indeed, it was from here that Marie Curie obtained pitchblende from which she isolated radium. The miners suffered from a strange disease known as 'Bergkranheit'. Eventually, it was realised that they were suffering from various forms of cancer. The table below compares the mortality rate of miners with the general population in the area.

	Deaths per 1000 population		
	Jachymow miners 1929–38	*Schneeberg miners 1895–1912*	*General population 1932–36*
Lung cancer	9.8	16.5	0.34
Other cancers	0.7	2.1	2.1

2 Use the data in the table to draw a histogram. *(5)*
3 How many times higher was the lung cancer rate for the
  (i) Jachymow
  (ii) Schneeberg
  miners when compared to the general population? *(2)*
4 Explain which mine you think might have had the higher level of radioactivity. *(2)*

The high frequency of lung cancers in the miners was due to the radioactive gas radon. This is produced by the decay of radium and diffuses into the atmosphere. The radon will in turn decay into solid radioactive substances such as polonium.

5 How does this information help explain why lung cancer was so high in the miners? *(2)*

The working conditions of the miners did not help. Often they were several miles away from their villages and had to walk to work with inadequate clothing and in bitterly cold weather. As a result they were prone to chest diseases and infection so that their lungs could not clean themselves properly.

6 How would this affect the miners? *(1)*

Early in 1986, a nuclear accident occurred at the atomic power station at Chernobyl in Russia. Soviet scientists calculate that 100 million curies (a measure of the amount of radioactivity) was released into the atmosphere. The amount released by the atomic bomb over Nagasaki was 1000 million curies. Among the gaseous radioactive contaminants that escaped were radioactive caesium and iodine. High levels of radiation not only cause long term effects such as cancer but also short term effects such as hair loss, vomiting and diarrhoea. This is largely due to the damage to dividing cells. Because of the delay in evacuating people from the area around the reactor, scientists estimate that some 6530 extra cancer deaths will occur in the area over the next 70 years. To help decontaminate the area, the top soil is being removed and replaced from a 1000 square miles surrounding the plant. The radioactivity has not only affected those near to the plant. A cloud of radioactive material passed over Europe, including Britain. As a result of heavy rainfall, much of the material in this was washed out and fell over north western England.

7 How many times greater was the amount of radioactivity released in the atomic bomb over Nagasaki compared to that from Chernobyl? *(1)*

8 Why was the top soil removed and replaced around the power station? *(1)*

9 In parts of England where rain fell that was contaminated with radioactivity, farmers were not allowed to sell their sheep. Why was this? *(2)*

10(a) The bone marrow contains many dividing cells. What type of cells are produced here? *(1)*

(b) What would happen if these cells stopped dividing for a while? *(1)*

Radioactive iodine may enter the food chain and if taken up by the body may be concentrated in the thyroid.

11 Why should it accumulate in the thyroid? *(1)*

Total 20 marks

55 *In vitro* fertilisation

Some couples have trouble conceiving a baby. This may be because the man has a low sperm count or because the woman has blocked oviducts (fallopian tubes). Such couples may now be able to have a 'test-tube baby'. First, the woman is given hormones to increase the number of eggs maturing in each ovary. When the eggs are about to be released from the surface of the ovary, they are collected. This is done by a doctor who uses a fine tube which is passed through the wall of the abdomen. The eggs are sucked up into the tube and transferred to a shallow glass dish. This contains a special culture (nutrient) solution. Semen from the man is added and fertilisation can then take place. Three days after fertilisation, embryos of eight or sixteen cells have formed. Two or three of these are then transferred to the uterus via the cervix. If the technique is successful, at least one of these embryos will implant and grow into a baby.

1   Why is it important to increase the number of eggs maturing in the ovaries? *(2)*

2(a) Assuming the woman has a regular menstrual cycle of 28 days, on which day in the cycle would the doctor look for eggs on the surface of the ovary? *(1)*

 (b) Why should the doctor want to collect the eggs at this time in the cycle? *(2)*

3   What must the culture solution provide in order to ensure the development of the eggs? *(3)*

4   What is meant by the term 'fertilisation'. *(2)*

5   Why is it important that the embryos are allowed to grow to the 8 or 16 cell stage before they are placed in the uterus? *(2)*

6   The eggs were removed by a tube passing through the wall of the abdomen. Why are the young embryos put back by a different technique? *(2)*

7   Why do some people object to the use of *in vitro* fertilisation? *(1)*

Total 15 marks

56 The growth of a cockroach

The table below shows the increase in mass of a cockroach (*Blatta germanica*).

Day 0–1 mg	Day 10– 4.6 mg	Day 22–17.0 mg
3–2.5 mg	13– 9.2 mg	27–35.0 mg
5–2.4 mg	15– 8.9 mg	29–29.0 mg
8–4.8 mg	19–18.5 mg	35–64.0 mg
		39–58.0 mg

1   Plot a graph of the data in the table.   *(5)*

2(a) The cockroach shows incomplete metamorphosis. Name another insect which shows a similar pattern of growth.   *(1)*

 (b) Mark on your graph one point when you think the cockroach has shed its exoskeleton. Explain why the insect is vulnerable at these times in its life cycle.   *(3)*

 (c) What is the name given to the stages by which the cockroach reaches the adult form.   *(1)*

 (d) Suggest one way in which the young insect is different from the adult.   *(1)*

3(a) Give three characteristics that distinguish insects from other animals.   *(3)*

 (b) Give one feature that insects, spiders and woodlice have in common.   *(1)*

Total 15 marks

57 Seeds and germination

The diagram below shows a section through a germinating pea seed.

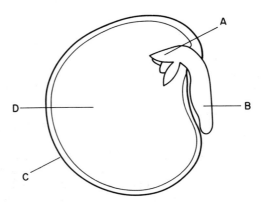

1   Match each statement below by using the letters on the
    diagram. You can use each letter once, more than once or
    not at all.
    (i) The part where food reserves are stored.
    (ii) Forms the embryo of the seed.
    (iii) Protects the seed.
    (iv) Will form the root of the plant.
    (v) Will form the shoot of the plant.   (5)
2   Use the following words to write a short account of the
    early stages of germination:
    *food reserves, enzymes, cotyledons (seed leaves), embryo,
    respiration*   (5)
3   As the seed germinates the embryo will grow to form parts
    of the mature plant. Growth requires the formation of new
    cells by mitosis. Name one part of the embryo where mitosis
    takes place.   (1)

The data in the table on page 81 shows the changes in dry mass
during the first 10 days of germination of a pea seed.

Days after germination	Mass (g)
0	0.54
2	0.53
4	0.50
6	0.48
8	0.46
10	0.48

4 Draw a graph of the results. (5)

5(a) What happens to the dry mass of the seed from day 0 to day 8? (1)

(b) Explain why this change occurs. (2)

6(a) What happens to the dry mass of the seed after day 8? (1)

(b) Explain why this happens. (3)

7 It is said that the juice of the fleshy part of a tomato inhibits the germination of tomato seeds. If you are given a supply of tomatoes, distilled water, cotton wool, petri dishes and a juice extractor and any other normal laboratory apparatus that you need, explain how you would test the statement by an experiment. (5)

8 Some seeds when dispersed from the parent plant are dormant. They are unable to germinate until they have been exposed to a period of low temperature. Explain why this is an advantage, especially in a climate like ours. (2)

Total 30 marks

58 The growth of marrow seedlings

Two marrow seedlings, A and B, were grown in separate containers in a well-lit and ventilated greenhouse. Seedling A was watered with distilled water throughout the experiment, but B was watered with a solution containing a commercial liquid fertilizer. The height of the seedlings was recorded.

Time in days	Height of seedling (mm)	
	A	B
0	0	0
4	52	43
8	60	49
12	70	75
16	95	105
20	180	200

1(a) Plot a graph of these results. (6)
 (b) What was the height of each plant on day 14? (2)
 (c) Work out the average growth per day of seedling A and seedling B throughout the period of the experiment. Show all your calculations clearly. (2)
 (d) Give one reason for using height as a measure of growth. (1)
 (e) Give one other way in which the growth of the plants could have been measured. (1)
2 The experimenter concluded that the fertilizer made seedling B grow faster. What other possible explanation for the results can you think of? (1)
3(a) Why is it important that the greenhouse should be ventilated? (2)
 (b) Give one reason why crops such as marrows and cucumbers may be grown in greenhouses. (1)
4 How would you improve upon the experimental procedure used in the investigation above? (4)

Total 20 marks

59 Flower pollination

The diagrams below show two flowers that are pollinated by different means. Flower 1 is much bigger than flower 2.

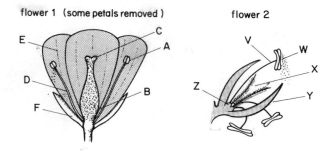

flower 1 (some petals removed)

flower 2

1(a) Match the letters (A–F) on flower 1 to that of the structure that has the same function in flower 2. You may use each letter once, more than once or not at all. (3)

(b) One of the plants is wind pollinated. Which one is it and how is it adapted? (2)

2 In flower 1 the male organs open and release their pollen before the stigma of the same flower is ready to receive them. Explain how this favours cross-pollination. (2)

3 Describe the sequence of events after pollination leading to fertilisation. (3)

A student wished to show that geranium flowers cannot form fruits unless they have been pollinated. He placed an unopened flower in a clear polythene bag so that nothing could get in. Each day he inspected it to see what had happened. Two weeks later, he was surprised to see that a fruit had appeared.

4(a) How might the flower have been pollinated? (1)

(b) What should the student have done to ensure that no pollination occurred? Explain your answer. (2)

(c) What would have been a suitable control for his experiment? (2)

Total 15 marks

83

60 Fruit dispersal

The diagram below shows some different fruits. A fruit is an ovary after fertilisation, containing seeds.

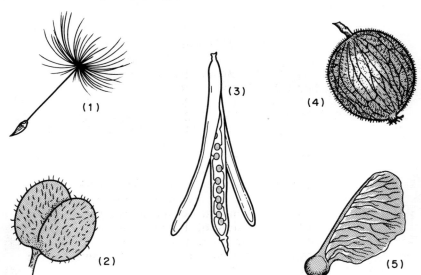

(1)
(2)
(3)
(4)
(5)

1(a) Give one difference between a fruit and a seed. (1)
 (b) A fruit like a tomato contains seeds with a hard seed coat
     (testa). Why do they have hard coats? (1)
2(a) Which of the fruits in the diagram is likely to be dispersed
     by:
     (i) wind
     (ii) animals
     (iii) an explosive mechanism? (5)
 (b) Suggest reasons for your choices for (i) and (ii) (4)
3(a) Suggest one advantage of dispersal of seeds from the parent
     plant. (1)
 (b) Suggest one disadvantage of dispersal of seeds from the
     parent plant. (1)
4   Why do seeds often become dormant for a period after they
     have been dispersed from the parent plant? (2)

Total 15 marks

61 Leaf variation

Some students collected leaves from a privet hedge growing in the school. The length of the leaves was carefully measured. The results are shown below.

						Lengths of the leaves (mm)								
8	5	18	26	12	19	20	19	14	6	24	16	25	8	9
17	7	26	10	20	7	18	9	16	31	11	23	18	15	21
11	30	21	23	30	13	19	22	24	24	28	27	17	25	23
32	25	20	21	29	27	23	22	28	20	26	22	33	26	24
19	10	22	27	34	29	10	21	15	28	25	30	31	17	24
23	21													

1   Plot a histogram of the number of leaves against the leaf length in mm. First divide the leaves into categories (5–8 mm, 9–12 mm etc.) and then count the number in each category. Use the results to plot the histogram. *(4)*

2(a) Give two reasons why the leaves vary in size. *(2)*

  (b) Briefly describe how you would investigate the causes of the variation for one of these? *(3)*

Another, smaller, batch of leaves had their length and width measured. The results are shown below.

Length (mm)	8	4	5	8	8	12	18	16	12	14
Width (mm)	16	5	8	8	12	16	26	22	20	20

3(a) Plot a graph of the data above with leaf length on the horizontal axis and leaf width on the vertical axis. *(5)*

  (b) What is the relationship between leaf length and leaf width? *(1)*

Total 15 marks

Scientists have found that the amount of bark of trees that is covered by lichens changes as you move further away from the centre of industrialised cities.

Distance from city centre (km)	% Lichen cover
1	1
5	3
8	22
11	45
16	65
19	75
23	75

1   Plot a graph of the data in the table   (5)

Measurements were also taken of the level of sulphur dioxide. In the centre of the city there were 200 micrograms per cubic metre of air and on the outskirts of the city the level measured was 65 micrograms per cubic metre of air.

2(a) Suggest a hypothesis to account for the change in the coverage of the bark by lichens.   (2)

  (b) Describe in outline how you might test your hypothesis experimentally.   (3)

The peppered moth is common in Britain and is found in collections made as long ago as the early 1800's. The moth has two distinctly different forms. One is a pale speckled grey and the other is a darker almost black form. The black form is called the *melanic* type. Until 1849, only the pale form was found in collections, but in that year a melanic moth was found and recorded near Manchester. By 1900, only 2% of the moths near Manchester were the pale form and 98% were black.

During the day, the moth rests on the bark of trees. If it does not blend in with its background, then it is likely that it will be eaten by birds. The pie charts on the map show the proportions of the melanic and pale forms in England and Wales. You can see that in different areas of the country there are different proportions of the two forms. When the black moths occur in an area it is said to be an example of *industrial melanism*.

3   What does 'industrial melanism' mean?   *(1)*

4   Only the pale form is found in the West Country (A) and North Wales (B). Around Manchester and Birmingham only the dark (melanic) form is found. Why do you think this happens?   *(3)*

5   In East Anglia (C) a lot of the land is used for farming and it is not industrialised. Why are so many dark (melanic) moths found compared to the number of pale moths?   *(2)*

6   What changes happened in this country during the last hundred years that might explain the rise in the numbers of the dark (melanic) form?   *(2)*

7   What effect do you think the introduction of the Clean Air Act and smokeless zones might have had on the proportions of the pale and dark (melanic) forms?   *(2)*

Total 20 marks

63 Selection in ladybirds

Pollution resulting from the industrial revolution gave rise to the conditions for the spread of melanic moths. Melanism also occurs in other groups of animals in industrial areas. For example, there is a melanic (black) form of a spider found only on the gasworks at Stockport.

A species of ladybird, known as the two spot ladybird, is also found to have a melanic or dark form. The dark form is black with red spots, whilst the other form is red with black spots. The condition seems to be controlled by a pair of alleles and the dark form of the allele is dominant. Ladybirds are eaten by birds, but only the Redstart eats them regularly. Even so there are not enough Redstarts to have a major effect on the populations of ladybirds. In London, about 10% of the ladybird population is dark or melanic, though in Harrogate the percentage is 75%. In Birmingham the percentage of dark forms has declined since the Clean Air Acts were introduced. It was originally thought that the normal (red) forms of the ladybird were affected by some chemical in smoke. Now it has been shown that dark ladybirds are better at surviving in cold and dark conditions than the red form.

1(a) What material in smoke would result in the darkening of tree trunks and other surfaces? *(1)*

(b) Name one process that would produce large amounts of smoke? *(1)*

2   Why would the black form of the spider be at an advantage in the gasworks at Stockport? *(1)*

3(a) To which group of animals does the ladybird belong? *(1)*

(b) Give one characteristic of this group of animals. *(1)*

4   What is the percentage of red ladybirds in:
(i) Harrogate
(ii) London? *(2)*

5   Explain how it is possible for two black ladybirds to produce both black and red offspring. Show clearly the genotypes of the parents and the offspring. *(4)*

6   Using the information in the passage explain why the percentage of black ladybirds has declined in Birmingham. *(3)*

7   Name one other area of the country, apart from those mentioned in the passage, which might be expected to have a high percentage of red forms. *(1)*

Total 15 marks

64 Selection in mice

Large numbers of mice were found living in a derelict farm building. They were either dark brown or grey in colour. The mice fed on seeds and plant material. A hole was made in the side of the building to allow cats to enter. Very rapidly the population of mice was reduced to one third of its former level. All the grey mice had disappeared. The cats' entrance was then sealed up again. The mouse population began to increase again and the light form of the mouse began to reappear.

1 Using the list below, select those words which describe the feeding relationships of:
  (i) the mice
  (ii) the cats.
      producers, prey, predators, decomposers, primary consumers, secondary consumers (4)

2 Darwin's book 'The Origin of Species by Means of Natural Selection' demonstrated the idea of the survival of the fittest. How can you explain the relationship of the mice and cats in this way? (3)

3 Why did the population of mice increase when the cats were excluded again? (1)

4 Assume that coat colour in mice is determined by a single pair of alleles and that D is the symbol for the allele that controls brown coat and d is the symbol for the allele that controls grey coat.
  (a) If a mouse is heterozygous (Dd), what coat colour is it? (1)
  (b) Assuming both its parents were homozygous, what would their genotypes be? (2)
  (c) Two grey mice were captured and bred. Explain with appropriate diagrams, what coat colour their offspring would have. (2)
  (d) Two brown mice were bred. They produced both brown and grey offspring. Explain how this could come about. (2)

In all your workings show clearly the genotypes and phenotypes of parents and the alleles carried by the gametes.

Total 15 marks

Answers to numerical questions

6 2(a)(i) 0700 (ii) 1500
7 1. 2.2% 4(a) 23 404 kJ 4(b) 21 436 kJ 5(a) 3056 kJ 5(b) 14.26%
6(a) 125 kJ 6(b) 7.35 g 6(c) 22.05 kg
8 1(a) 24.36%
11 2(b)(i) 23.73% (ii) 42.86%
12 4. 5 times
15 6(a)(i) 593 males (ii) 17 females 6(b) 293 deaths
16 1. Prison 1 36 cases, Prison 2 60 cases, Prison 3 35 cases,
Prison 4 53 cases, Prison 5 65 cases
19 2(i) 200 million 3(a) 18 hours
25 1. 3.97 kg 2. 75 kg 4. 48 kg 5. 13 kg 6. 9.1 kg 7. 38.9 kg
26 2. Africa 77.55%, Asia 78.72%, Europe 43.02%,
North America 33.33%
30 3(a)(i) 4% carbon dioxide (ii) 16% oxygen (iii) 80% nitrogen
32 5(i) 13.5% (ii) 25.8%
33 4(i) 0.3 s faster (ii) 0.7 s faster (iii) 45 s slower
(iv) 55.2 s slower
35 2(a)(i) 232.6 cm^3 (ii) 115.9 cm^3 2(b)(i) 237.4 cm^3 (ii) 118.1 cm^3
36 4(a) 5000 kJ 4(b) 27.78%
37 1(a)(i) 36.0 °C (ii) 36.4 °C 1(b)(i) 37.0 °C (ii) 37.7 °C
42 2(a) 7 g per hour
44 1(a) Tray 1: 55% increase, Tray 2: 55% increase,
Tray 3: 110% increase
46 7(a)(i) 23 (ii) 23 (iii) 46
47 1(c)(i) 10.4% (ii) 33.6%
48 1(a)(i) 40 cm (ii) 13 cm (iii) 7 cm (iv) 16 cm 1(b) birth–2 years
49 3(a)(i) Europe 115.04% (ii) Africa 133.68%
3(b)(i) Europe 21.5% (ii) Africa 49.55%
50 1(a) 38.2 million 1(b) 57.7 million 3(a) 7.59% 3(b) 19.76% 4(a)
58.12%
51 2. 25.73%
53 1(b) 0.5 2(b) 0.25
54 2(i) approx. 29 times (ii) approx. 49 times 6. 10 times
58 1(c) Seedling A. 9mm/day Seedling B: 10 mm/day
63 4(i) 25% (ii) 90%

British Library Cataloguing in Publication Data

Liffen, C. L.
    Structured questions for GCSE biology.
    1. Biology——Examinations, questions, etc.
    I. Title   II. Liffen, C. F.
    574'.076   QH316

ISBN 0 340 41483 9

First printed 1987

Typeset by Photo·graphics, Honiton, Devon
Printed in Great Britain for Hodder and Stoughton Educational, a division of Hodder
and Stoughton Ltd, Mill Road, Dunton Green, Sevenoaks, Kent by Biddles Ltd,
Guildford and King's Lynn